C000231712

Urban
Permaculture

David Watkins

Permanent Publications

Published by
Permanent Publications
Hyden House Limited
Little Hyden Lane
Clanfield
Hampshire
PO8 0RU
England
Tel: (0705) 596500
Fax: (0705) 595834

Design and typesetting by
Tim Harland, Permanent Publications

Cover illustration by
Paul Butler

Illustrations by
David Watkins and Tim Harland

Printed by
Woolnough Bookbinding Limited
Irthlingborough, Northamptonshire

British Library Cataloguing in Publication Data
A catalogue record for this book is available from the British Library

ISBN 1 85623 002 3

A voluntary Tree Tax on the paper used in the production of this book is paid
into a special fund for tree planting projects. Submissions for grants may be
made to the Permaculture Association (Britain). Grants are available for seed
and tree stock only.

CONTENT

THE AUTHOR

David Watkins has led a rich and varied life. He initially studied science, then specialised in design, working professionally both as an interior designer and in the theatre. He then lectured on three dimensional design at art college and later trained in computing and computer aided design. At the same time, he pursued his lifelong interest in ceramics and held a number of exhibitions of his work. Recently, he trained as a masseur and also works in the field of humanistic psychology.

In 1983, David moved to an organic smallholding and obtained the Soil Association symbol, a guarantee to the consumer of the highest quality organic produce. The smallholding also required extensive building work, which he designed and built himself. In 1990, he wrote and self published the acclaimed book, *The Concise Book of Organic Growing & Small Livestock*. Other books by the author include *Living Outdoors* and *Exploring & Finding the Way*.

When he discovered permaculture, David was instantly inspired by its practical approach and positive attitude towards creating a sustainable future. He recognised it as an ideal framework with which to combine and use all his diverse skills and knowledge. David is now teaching permaculture design courses throughout Britain and is a council member of the Permaculture Association (Britain) and associate editor of *Permaculture Magazine*.

INTRODUCTION

I have frequently heard people say that it is all very well talking about permaculture, but that they cannot afford a large piece of land. The fundamental point to permaculture is that everyone can do it, and start doing it now, regardless of the ownership of land. This is because permaculture is an attitude and a holistic approach to how we lead our lives, rather than just a method of growing food.

This book is intended to provide a basic outline to some of the simple, down to earth ways in which you can practise permaculture principles and how to apply them, starting in your own home. This does not mean returning to a frugal lifestyle. In many ways it is quite the contrary, as the practice of permaculture will enable you to lead a much richer, more bountiful and conscious way of life. After all, the more we can take personal responsibility for ourselves and the impact we have on the world, the more chance we have of a future for the human race.

Urban Permaculture has been prompted by the good permaculture principle of sharing information. In turn, I should like to thank all the many people who have shared information with me. This book is dedicated to them and to the growing number of caring people who are working together towards the real possibility of a sustainable future.

1

WHAT IS PERMACULTURE?

Permaculture encourages people to take responsibility for themselves, to gain more control of their lives and to take positive steps towards achieving a sustainable future. It is not just for people with land, everyone can play their part.

Our culture today has evolved from the industrial revolution. In the process, it has exercised an increasing and unthinking dominance over nature, making use of and exploiting everything our environment has to offer. We now realise that this indiscriminate waywardness is endangering the well-being and natural resources of our planet and could ultimately lead to our extinction. The industrial might of the 'developed' countries has also grown from the ruthless exploitation of people. As a result, we are now starting to experience not only the breakdown of our ecosystem, but also of the human society globally.

Permaculture was developed in Australia in the 1970s by Bill Mollison and David Holmgren. The word 'permaculture' is derived from 'permanent agriculture' which inevitably became 'permanent culture'. It is a highly positive and creative approach to finding solutions for a sustainable future for the world and its inhabitants. Its fundamental principles are based on the twin concepts of *people care* and *Earth care*. If we care about people we will automatically care for the Earth. It is a design approach which combines appropriate knowledge and technology to make the most of any given situation. It is inevitably eclectic, including a synthesis of many ecologically sound principles, old and new methods and technologies, and whatever is appropriate for any particular circumstance.

The majority of people live in an urban environment. It is therefore of the utmost importance to introduce permaculture into urban settings to counter the tremendous consumption of resources, production of waste and the ever decreasing quality of life.

PERMACULTURE PRINCIPLES

Permaculture is concerned with creating systems that are sustainable. The concept of sustainability encompasses many areas of our lives, whether it be our social systems, our sense of fullness and satisfaction in living, what we consume or the energy we expend. The primary ethic is to take responsibility; responsibility for ourselves, our children and our community.

Ethics

People care is concerned with providing all the necessities for our existence. These include our physical, emotional, intellectual, spiritual and social needs.

Earth care follows naturally from people care. If we truly care for people we will inevitably be caring for the environment. If we care for our environment and our children, we will be caring for the future well-being of every living and non living thing.

If we value these fundamental tenets, while we are 'putting our own houses in order' and designing our systems to the best of our ability, we can also contribute our surplus of time, money, information and energy to help others. People care and Earth care are inextricably linked and permeate every aspect of our lives. But unlike many of the prevailing human systems, they require co-operation rather than competition.

Some of the Permaculture Principles:

* Assume responsibility. This applies within yourself and within your community.

* Work with rather than against nature. Observe nature and learn. Study and use natural systems that are productive.

* The problem is the solution. See a solution, rather than a problem, and you will find a positive use for what was initially considered the problem.

* Be energy efficient. This applies to every aspect of your life. Energy should be used for useful, productive purposes.

* Make the least possible change for the greatest possible effect. Do not make unnecessary changes.

* Replace an equal or greater resource than is used.

* Minimum input for maximum output. Design a system so that it needs little work once established.

* Pollution is an unused output. Design systems to use everything. Recycle all wastes.

* Use biological resources. They are renewable if properly designed and managed.

* Use natural and biological energy systems. These include sun, wind, wave, water, biogas (i.e. methane) and biomass (i.e. wood).

* Create polycultural diversity for a productive interactive system. This makes a system more flexible in the face of change.

* Combine different elements in beneficial relationships with each other. To use outputs and conserve or recycle energy.

* Yield is theoretically unlimited. There is always something else that can be added to a system.

* Each element performs many functions. Take any element and see how many things it can do or be used for.

* When designing, make mistakes on paper. Spend time on research and planning.

PEOPLE CARE

First of all, we must be able to care for ourselves if we are to care for other people. If we can care for each other, we will then care about the world we live in and what future generations will inherit as a natural consequence. It seems to me that if we are to have any sort of sustainable future, it is of paramount importance that we take the responsibility for this care on all levels.

Personal Responsibility

The more responsibility we take, the more control of our lives we have. The more control we have, the more independent we are and the less demands we make on the system. The more involvement we have in life, the more we learn and understand in return. This gives us a much richer and fuller life because the more we put into life, the more fulfilling, fun and meaningful it will become. The more we co-operate and work with others in enriching pursuits, the better life becomes for everyone.

In taking personal responsibility, we also take care of ourselves. Such self care encompasses all aspects of ourselves; the physical, emotional, intellectual, spiritual and social. When we care for ourselves, we start to value ourselves and from that comes the valuing of others. We cannot love others if we do not care for ourselves.

Health

Health is a positive state that has to be worked at. It is much more than not being ill. It depends on lifestyle, eating, drinking, smoking, weight control, exercise, sleep, medical care, stress management, leisure, caring and security. Exercise makes us feel good as well as keeping the body working well. It does not have to be too strenuous. Swimming exercises most muscle groups and the lungs without creating stress, whilst yoga is very relaxing and keeps us supple at the same time.

Walking, cycling and gardening are good permaculture exercises as they can perform many functions at the same time. Stress management is very important. It is commonly accepted that the state of the mind can govern the health of the body. Yoga, meditation, Tai Chi and massage are good ways of dissipating negative states of mind. Massage has the additional advantage that it requires the touch of another caring human being. It is an ideal skill to share with family and friends. In addition, any tactile or manipulative skills will increase our pleasure in life, whether it is in woodworking or lovemaking.

By learning first aid and how to deal with simple ailments you can avoid putting an unnecessary additional load on the health service. A working knowledge of homoeopathy is useful as a first line of defence against common ailments. Herbs from the garden can also have therapeutic and medicinal value, although, as with all forms of medicine, you should treat them with respect as they can be potent healers.

Emotional Health

Emotional development allows us to experience our lives with appropriate emotions and with more energy. It frees us to have richer, clearer and more honest relationships. What influences us in a negative way, such as outmoded patterns of behaviour, fears and borrowed belief systems, usually originates in the past. They are a heritage of behaviours that are often no longer appropriate. Whether we are aware of them or not, they influence how we think, feel about ourselves, relate to others and how we live now.

Along with this baggage often comes a preoccupation with what might happen in the future. But we have only a limited amount of energy. If too much energy is invested in the past and in the future, how much is left for the 'now', the only point in which we really live? If we kick out the baggage from the past and the major investments in the 'mights', then we can use most of our energy to live more fully in the present. Rabbi Blue was once asked why he never seemed to worry. He replied that the things that he had worried about never seemed to happen; it was always something else that happened, so he gave up worrying.

Fun and Pleasure

Fun and pleasure are essential elements in our lives. They can be experienced on our own or usually with other people. It may also require some level of skill which will be rewarded by a sense of achievement. Many activities entail giving, receiving or both. Try making a list of the things that give you pleasure. Then write down how much they cost and when you last did them. You may be surprised at how many cost little or nothing. Give yourself a treat at least once a week.

Learning New Skills

There are times in life when the acquisition of new skills through study and training can contribute to the health of a person. Intellectual development and stimulation are a necessary part of the development of our skills and knowledge. Clarity in thought can allow us to see the world more clearly. This helps us to assess and solve problems which in turn add to the overall well-being of our lives. Knowledge can enhance our appreciation of things and further enrich our lives. Knowledge of a piece of music, for example, will add to our appreciation of a concert, or of growing plants to our visiting a garden.

Valuing Ourselves

It is important to value ourselves. How can we love others if we do not first love ourselves? From a regard for ourselves comes a regard for our needs. If we can honestly express our own needs, listen to others' and negotiate solutions, we can establish more open, honest, relationships. All these qualities require personal autonomy and self reliance, both of which come from the inner person.

To achieve these qualities is not easy and can be a painful process, but it is certainly worthwhile. There is now a whole industry catering for personal development, some of which is very expensive. One system which does not cost anything is co-counselling. This can be practised by anyone. The first step is to attend a fundamentals course. Thereafter, two individuals can arrange to meet and share an exchange that is mutually beneficial.

Spiritual

Spirituality gives meaning to everything. Everyone's perception of what spirituality is, is deeply personal. It can be expressed as love, creativity, nature, the universal creator. Spirituality is what puts us in touch with our soul and is what we experience in the high points in our lives. The more we are in touch with it, the more bountiful our lives become.

Community

We are essentially social beings and all of us need to have relationships and be members of groups. It is important for us to belong and be cared about. The more we can share with others, the more interpersonal experiences we have and the more chance we have for beneficial, mutual exchanges. A distillation of what a number of older people have said to me is, 'When you look back at life you will not focus on your solo activities. What you will remember are the incidents of touching, those times when your life was enriched by a moment of sharing with a friend or loved one'.

We all need close companionship, a sense of purpose and the ability to see the importance and value of what we are doing. These needs can all be fulfilled by working within a community.

The development and re-establishment of communities is seen as one of the goals of permaculture. Within a co-operative rather than competitive community, we have the opportunity for sharing, working together, supporting each other and developing the way of life that we want. Co-operation allows the community to take responsibility for many aspects of life. Far more can be achieved by a group than by the same number of individuals separately and it can be more fun.

Communities can not only provide bulk purchasing power with a necessity such as food, but also create employment and the opportunity for job sharing. For instance, consider a community orchard or plant nursery. Both could create many jobs and serve the people of the community and beyond. Likewise, a bakery, wholefood, garage or community exchange shop. Most communities encompass a variety of skills and knowledge, from darning to computer programming.

Consider what leisure and entertainment is needed. This could be a hall or rooms for meetings or concerts, a swimming pool or a sauna to every twenty households or a natural health clinic. What provision is there for those who need care? It would be cheaper and better for elderly people to band together to provide their own accommodation and hire their own staff to enable them to remain within the community. People with infirmities and disabilities could also be included in this scheme. We do not need to create retired and disabled ghettos. Nurseries and schools can also be run by the community to provide what we think is a proper education. All of these suggestions provide opportunities for employment and job sharing, as well as creating a diverse environment which enhances the strength of the whole.

What are the benefits of community ownership? Sharing resources can be much more economical in cash and environmental terms. Sharing workshops can allow for professional standards of tools with shared costs. Large equipment that is only occasionally used, such as a rotavator or welding gear, would make sense when shared communally. Likewise, equipment such as computers, photocopiers, printing facilities, minibuses and vans. Also, laundries and cold stores would be much more economic to run communally rather than individually. The possibilities and benefits of sharing are potentially enormous. Of course, a community would also share its joys and sorrows. All of these activities would help to bring people together and create a caring community.

A friend of mine once defined the ideal job description, which delighted me, as follows: 'Enough cash to get by on with a bit of surplus. A bit of fun and pleasure. A variety of activities. Always learning something new and a worthwhile end product.' This has always struck me as a good basic specification for life. I would, however, like to blur the distinction between work and leisure. To me, it also suggests having a variety of activities or employment to meet these ends and, of course, a beautiful environment.

Putting Our Houses In Order

4

CHANGING OUR OUTLOOK

As with everything, we are looking for minimum input and output in the home. Where possible, recycle everything on site or nearby. Look at what comes in and what goes out of the system. This includes everything such as people, energy, water, food, waste, clothes, materials, furnishings, consumer items and fittings.

Reducing your inputs and outputs lessens your impact on the environment and gives you more independence. You need less cash and, therefore, you do not need to spend so much time working to earn it! Or you could do a more worthwhile and satisfying job that pays less. Some things do take effort and are quite major changes, whilst others are small changes that are more about the way that you do things. But they all have an impact. The greatest impact will be on you as your way of life changes and with it your attitudes. As with everything else, do not try to make all the changes at once. First, plan what you want to do and make the changes gradually. Changing your whole lifestyle in one fell swoop can be daunting. Be gentle with yourself and ease into it when and if you want to. If you have an overall, as well as detailed plan, you will always have something to do if you want to and it will prevent you from having to re-do things that do not fit into the long term plan. However, you will need to remain flexible and open to change as your ideas and information change.

Many people rush around, working long hours so they can buy more labour saving devices, then working even longer hours to run, maintain and replace them. It has been said that in our society there are a lot of people working to buy things that they do not really want, with money they do not have, to impress people that do not care.

With a simpler way of life, there are less demands on your time and money. This in turn can lessen the stress in your life and allow you to put your energies into more satisfying and worthwhile things such as yourself, your family, friends and community. Many activities can be done as a group which can make them easier and more fun.

5

ENERGY

Almost all of the energy we use is derived from non-renewable resources. Much of it is wasted. If we can cut our consumption of energy, be more efficient about what we use and use renewable resources, we are moving some way towards sustainability.

It is useful to look at indirect as well as direct energy consumption. Using electricity is inefficient as it is an indirect secondary power source. Due to loss in the production and distribution process, we only achieve about 30% of the original input of energy.

When purchasing goods, we are paying for the energy used in the production, distribution, packaging and advertising. It makes sense, therefore, not only to buy less but also to purchase items which have incurred minimal processing and have been produced locally. For instance, the good sense of this is demonstrated when we contrast buying a processed frozen food product with a locally produced organic food product that can be eaten raw. The processed item has used energy in its growing, production, packaging (production, processing and subsequent disposal), storage, transportation (including bringing in the various ingredients), distribution and cooking. It will probably also be an inferior product in taste and nutrition. The locally produced organic seasonal product will be fresh. The energy used in its production is minimal and transportation costs non-existent if collected on foot or by bicycle. The cash is also kept in the community and there is human contact between the grower and the consumer. It is useful to look at every aspect of what we buy; its durability, what it requires to produce and deliver it, as well as if we really need it.

Cutting Consumption

In a house, one of the highest consumers of energy is heating the house and its water. Initially, one should concentrate on using less. This can be done in a number of ways such as reducing demand and waste. Firstly, look at the temperatures you are maintaining. Could it be cooler? We do not have to live in our shirtsleeves in the winter! Maybe your living spaces could be upstairs and sleeping space downstairs as heat rises and there is usually more light and a better view upstairs. You do not need such a high temperature in bedrooms. To cut heat loss, you can insulate the building where possible and stop drafts. This includes windows which, if not double or secondary glazed, can have insulating shutters or curtains. An alternative is to have exterior greenhouses fitted to the windows. Entrances can have porches to reduce heat loss. All hot water systems should have insulated tanks and pipework.

If you have radiators, they should be controlled by individual thermostats. For water heating, instantaneous gas or electric water heaters will heat only the water required on demand. The simplest way to cut consumption is just to use less hot water and not have it at such a high temperature.

Look at the appliances used in a house and what the power consumption is. Lighting can use a surprising amount of electricity; use energy saving bulbs. A freezer that is constantly running can use large amounts of electricity, especially older models. Keep it in a cool place and use an energy saving plug especially designed for freezers and fridges. Do you really need a tumble drier? Would it be better to have a drying rack on the kitchen ceiling or in the airing cupboard or loft? With a cooker, do not continue to boil on a high setting when simmering on a low setting will work just as well. Keep the lid on pots to contain the heat. If using the oven, plan to cook on all shelves. Maybe use waterless cookware, a wok, pressure cooker or hay box which all save energy. Do not fill the kettle up for one cup.

Everything adds up. It is often easier to use human power rather than a machine and you get satisfaction and exercise from cutting the grass, sawing, planing or travelling by pedal power.

Heat can be obtained from sustainable sources. A fire or stove can also have a back boiler to heat the water and a place for a kettle. Some modern stoves like Agas can be used for cooking, space and water heating, food drying and many other things. An alternative is a type of stove that has been used for a long time in Europe, the kachelofen. This is positioned in the centre of the house and has a large mass. It is heated by a fire of coppiced small section wood, which flares up to produce a fierce heat. The convoluted flue allows all the heat to be absorbed by the oven's mass which radiates it gently until the next fire is lit.

Have a trellis covered in an evergreen climbing plant, like ivy, on outside walls of the house (a method called biotexturing), to conserve heat by stopping wind chill and chilling by evaporation from wet render or brickwork. Ivy will not damage a brick wall if the pointing is good. If you have a tile or slate roof it will need to be trimmed at the eaves to stop damage.

Solar panels are useful to preheat the hot water system. This is significant even in the winter. Care should be taken to place them at the right angle and facing the sun. Passive solar heating is achieved by having large windows on the south side or a conservatory. A conservatory can also be used to create a cooling draught in the summer.

In any glazed structure which relies on maximum sun penetration (such as solar panels or greenhouses), the angle of the glass should be at right angles to the sun to present the maximum area and create minimal reflection. As heat gain is more necessary in the winter, it is more important to get the angle right for winter sunlight.

In 1817, the Rev. Thomas Wilkinson put this into a formula: "The angle between the wall and the glass should be equal to the complement of the latitude, plus or minus the value for the sun's declination on the day when the sun's rays are to be perpendicular."

An example:
Day chosen for the rays to fall perpendicular: 1st February
Latitude: 52° 30'
Complement of latitude: 90° - 52° 30' = 37° 30'
Declination for 1st February: 17° 12'
ANGLE = 20° 18'

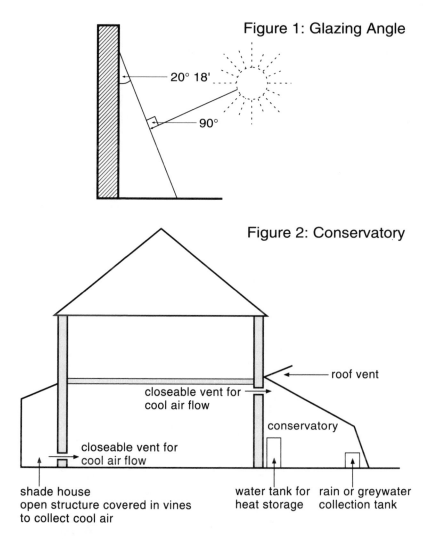

Figure 1: Glazing Angle

20° 18'

90°

Figure 2: Conservatory

roof vent

closeable vent for
cool air flow

conservatory

closeable vent for
cool air flow

shade house
open structure covered in vines
to collect cool air

water tank for
heat storage

rain or greywater
collection tank

A conservatory on the south side of a house can have many benefits. It can provide insulation, passive solar heating in the winter and a good growing area. Collected heat can be conserved in water tanks, and vents in the wall can be opened to let heat into the house. In summer the updraft from the roof vent can be used to create a through cooling draft. It can be shaded in the summer by growing plants up the outside, such as a grape vine or beans. Deciduous trees can be planted on the sun side to cast shade, allowing light in the winter.

Solar Panels

The conventional method of heating water by using the sun's energy is with solar panels. The panels are usually positioned on roofs, or on walls where they can act as a canopy over a window. They should be positioned facing the equator and the angle should approximately equal the angle of the latitude that you are on; a slightly higher angle will allow for the angle of the sun in winter. If more than one panel is used they should be connected in parallel. If a non pumping system is required, the panels should be positioned below the level of the hot water tank and minimum 28mm pipes used as this is needed to allow sufficient water flow. The hot water is usually circulated through an indirect preheat cylinder or through a coil of copper pipe in the hot water header tank to preheat the water.

Panels can be easily constructed using an insulated container with a glazed top. Placed inside this is a black painted central heating radiator to circulate the water through, or an undulating pipe on a black painted metal panel. The fluid should contain anti-freeze in the winter and be independent from other systems.

Figure 3: Possible Positions for Solar Panels

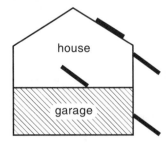

Figure. 4: Parallel Plumbed Solar Panels

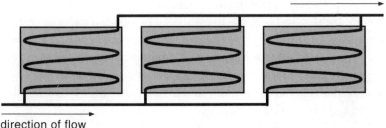

direction of flow

18

Figure 5: Typical Solar Hot Water Plumbing

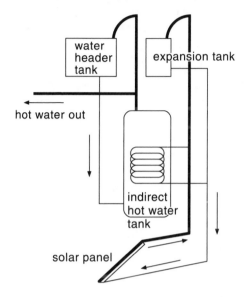

water
header
tank

expansion tank

hot water out

indirect
hot water
tank

solar panel

Figure 6: Bread Box Solar Water Heating

roof space lined
and insulated;
with access door

rooflight or
double glazed
roof section

hot water out

direct water
cylinder
painted black

cold water in

This system comprises a hot water cylinder painted black, positioned in a sealed, insulated and glazed section of the roof. It can be plumbed directly into the hot water system or circulated through an indirect cylinder connected to the hot water system.

Roof Conversion

A roof can be an ideal place to have a greenhouse. It is only necessary to glaze the south side. If the roof is raised, it gives the additional advantages of more usable height and rainwater collection directly off the glass into the roof space. Plants can be grown throughout the year in this space if a growlux tube is used to supplement the shorter winter daylight hours. Grey water output can be used with the plants taking out the nutrients. Heat collected in the winter and stored in water tanks can be blown down to the rest of the house through trunking by using a fan. With the vent open in summer the roof greenhouse will draw cool air throughout the house from a shade house on the north side. Glass is also cheaper than conventional roofing.

Figure 7: Section Through House

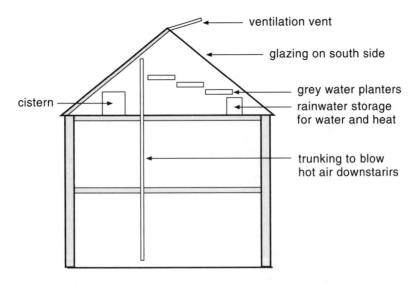

Figure 8: Alternative Section of Roof with Raised Side

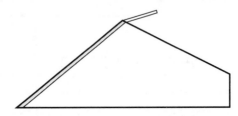

20

Cooking

The hay box is an old device for economical cooking. Food is brought to the boil in a pot and placed in a sealed insulated container. It is then left during the day or overnight to cook. The only energy used is during the initial boiling.

To make a hay box, first you need to make a heatproof container to fit the pot. This could be made of thin plywood, lino or metal. This is then clad with a minimum of 10cm thick insulation, preferably 15cm, including a well fitting lid. Insulation materials could be shredded paper, hay, straw, vermiculite, feathers, cork, expanded polystyrene, fleece or a vegetable fibre such as from the head of a bulrush. I have seen soft hay boxes like a duvet with a metalised fabric cover which is buttoned round the pot.

Figure 9: Hay Box

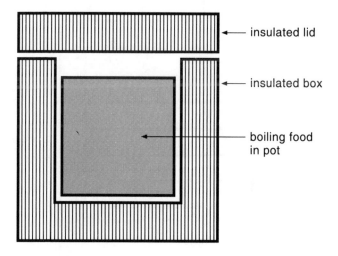

← insulated lid

← insulated box

← boiling food in pot

21

Heating and Cooking

The Kachelofen has been used for centuries throughout northern Europe. It is fired up twice a day with small section wood which fires up to a very high temperature. This means that there is no precipitation of tars. The heat rises through a convoluted flue which heats up the mass of the stove which radiates the heat during the rest of the day. The stove is often positioned in the centre of the house projecting into different rooms. Because of the need for small section fuel it is possible to use kindling that falls naturally from mature trees or clearings from plantation tidying. Another source could be from coppicing.

Figure 10: The Kachelofen

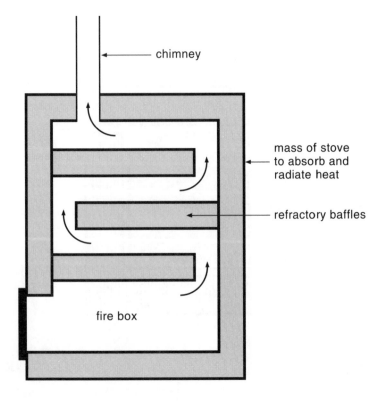

chimney

mass of stove to absorb and radiate heat

refractory baffles

fire box

6

WATER

An ever increasing quantity of water is consumed, and wasted, in our society. As we use more and more, we are destroying our waterways and depleting reserves of ground water faster than they are being replenished.

We are also contaminating our water with domestic and industrial waste which is then cleaned by adding more chemicals. Contaminated water that cannot be cleaned pollutes our waterways and then finally the sea. The quality of our water is deteriorating and there is general concern about the chemicals and microbes it increasingly contains and their effect upon us. Pollutants found in our water include nitrates, pesticides, chlorine, aluminium, drug residues, fluoride, detergents, bacteria and lead. Our concerns are about the quantities used, its quality and its contamination. Water may soon be metered, so saving it will save us money too.

Practical Steps to Take

We can use less. We can reuse what we have and we can collect it. We can try to improve the quality of what we drink. The collection and use of grey water is not legal in Great Britain. Grey water is the water from baths, basins and showers whilst black water contains urine and fecal matter.

Using Less

Whilst average consumption of water varies, it is approximately 140 litres a head per day. Of this, 43 litres are flushed down the toilet, 55 litres are used for personal hygiene, 21 litres for laundry and only about 4 litres for drinking and cooking.

To save water with the toilet, a dual flush cistern can be installed. A greater saving can be made by flushing only solids, using white vinegar to descale the pan. If a large plastic container with a large funnel is placed beside the toilet for collecting urine, it can then be poured away in one flush a day. It can, of course, also be diluted with water and used on the garden as it is a good, sterile and balanced fertiliser. It can also be put on the compost heap as urine is a great compost activator and speeds up the composting process. A further saving can be made by using a compost toilet for the solids.

To save water generally, turn down the water pressure to reduce the flow. Try not to wash anything under running water. Use a mug of water for teeth. For washing or shaving, put water in the basin. Use a bath half full or, better still, use a shower. When using a shower, wet yourself first, turn off when soaping and then rinse off. You can also buy water-saving shower and tap heads. Wash the car using a bucket and watering can of rainwater. Use plenty of mulch and close ground cover in the garden to minimise water loss. If possible, use trickle hoses with rainwater.

Reusing

Waste water from basins, baths and showers can be collected and used to flush w.c.s. All grey water can be collected, filtered and used to water the garden, although care must taken with what goes into the water: use only ecologically sound products. The grey can go straight onto the garden from a collection tank or, if 3" perforated pipes are buried in the soil, it can go direct to the roots. Grey water can pass through a tank for heat collection, or through a greenhouse, conservatory or glazed roof section to raise the heat level, and be used for hydroponic growing.

Collecting

If you have a well or spring, this can be easy if it proves to be safe. It is essential to have the water tested by your local water company. This is unlikely to be drinkable in either town or country because of the contamination of ground and surface water, as well as from impurities in the rainfall.

Rainwater can be collected off roofs and stored in covered

barrels or tanks and used either in the garden or in every case except for drinking and cooking. If filtered and stored properly, it is possible to drink it if the air is reasonably clean. It is better, however, to use solar distillation and then remineralise it by putting a bit of limestone in it. Ensure that any patio or paved area has spaces for rainwater to drain into the soil or is permeable.

Improving the Quality of Water

Drinking water should be filtered, but this can be expensive. The cheapest method is to use a filter jug, but they are made of plastic and the filters frequently need to be replaced. The other alternative is to have plumbed in filtration. Before purchasing a fixed filtration system, obtain an analysis from your water company to see what is in the water then check the laboratory tests from the filter manufacturers. Make sure that the two readings are compatible.

The types of filters available include:

1) Distillation.
   Expensive in energy if a solar system is not used.

2) Activated carbon filter.
   Can encourage bacterial growth if not changed correctly.

3) Reverse osmosis.
   Uses a membrane that filters under pressure.

One of the best solutions for filtration could be a solar still. The stills obtained from climbing and hiking shops for survival hikes are the cheapest to use or are useful as a model.

Figure 11: Rainwater Collection

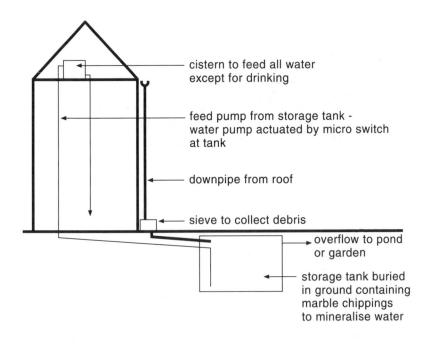

cistern to feed all water except for drinking

feed pump from storage tank - water pump actuated by micro switch at tank

downpipe from roof

sieve to collect debris

overflow to pond or garden

storage tank buried in ground containing marble chippings to mineralise water

Figure 12: Cistern in Loft

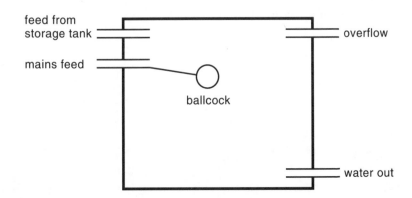

feed from storage tank

mains feed

overflow

ballcock

water out

Grey Water Treatment

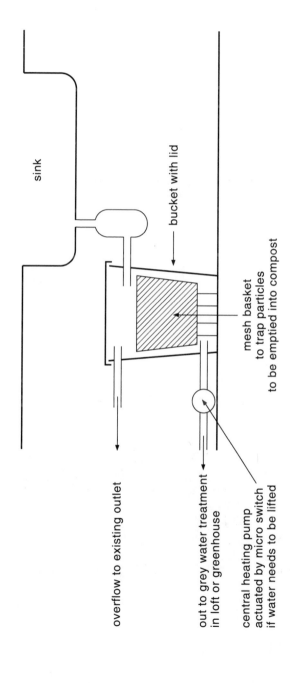

Figure 13: Grey Water Collection from Under Sink

27

Figure 14: Section of Grey Water Filtration System

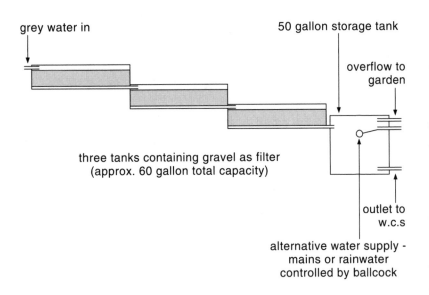

grey water in

50 gallon storage tank

overflow to garden

three tanks containing gravel as filter
(approx. 60 gallon total capacity)

outlet to
w.c.s

alternative water supply -
mains or rainwater
controlled by ballcock

Figure 15: Section Through Filter Tank

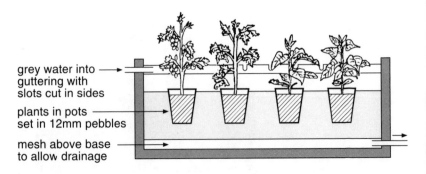

grey water into
guttering with
slots cut in sides

plants in pots
set in 12mm pebbles

mesh above base
to allow drainage

Ideal Community Water System

Industrial waste should be treated separately to community waste to minimise the risk of contamination. Drinking water can be supplied to the kitchen sink and treated water for other uses supplied elsewhere. Care needs to be taken with what goes into the waste water. Grey water and rainwater are returned to the treatment plant. The black water is returned to a sewage plant where it goes through a methane digester and is then treated in reed beds. The treated water is then returned to the system for industrial use or for watering, and the treated sewage is returned to the land.

Figure 16: Ideal Community Water System

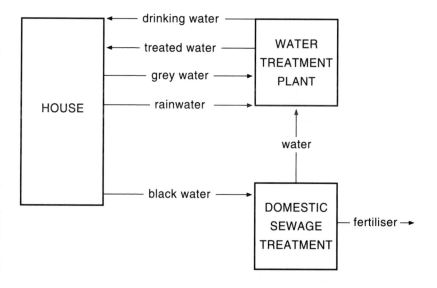

7

WASTE

There is no such thing as waste. Waste is an unused or unwanted resource. When it occurs we should see how we can eliminate, minimise, use or recycle it.

We should also consider the unnecessary consumption of resources and energy in terms of waste. Likewise, the inefficient or inappropriate use of personal energy. It is therefore necessary to define and question what is waste. Is cycling or playing tennis a waste? Is having fun or relaxing a waste?

Taking Control

Initially, we need to control what comes into the house. Avoid disposable goods such as razors, nappies, plastic cups and paper napkins. Use products that do not pollute. Buy basic products with minimal packaging and buy only what you really need rather than what has a passing appeal. Buy quality goods that are produced in an ecologically aware manner, have a long life, are economical to run and are easily repairable. This will be cheaper in the long run and better in all other ways.

Cutting Down

You can cut down on waste by using less and by the more efficient use of it (as in the case of water and energy) and by collecting or producing your own (as with water and food). Actions such as the judicious use of the car, switching off lights, keeping the house cooler, using hand tools rather than power tools and sharing will all save energy.

Reuse

Reuse does not use energy. Buy second-hand goods or exchange them. Car boot sales generate income and the reuse of unwanted items. Charity shops are good for clothes. A local community boutique could be a place where unwanted clothing, furniture and any other goods can be deposited and you take what you need.

There are many things that can be reused. The only limit is your imagination. Reusing envelopes is another example. Just reseal with sticky tape and cross out the old address. This saves the waste of buying sticky printed labels. Reuse bottles, containers and jars for your own produce or storage. Some healthfood stores will fill your containers. If they do not, ask them why not? Schools and workshops may take your excess; they often need containers for storage or mixing things in.

Repair and Refurbishment

Reuse can also be achieved by repair or refurbishment. Nowadays the attitude seems to be to throw things away if they are not perfect. Clothes, furniture and many household items can be repaired. Obtain items that are made of materials and a construction that will allow repair. Learn the repair skills. This could later generate income.

Recycling

Recycling is slowly getting under way, at least in the case of aluminium, newspaper and glass. Metals have always had a market if they are sorted. But do you need to buy newspapers? If so, you could insist on them being thinner. Do you really need to buy products using aluminium cans? Recycling can require additional energy consumption which can simply be avoided if such items are not bought in the first place!

In the home, you will need to allow for recycling as part of your waste management. In the kitchen, separate containers can be organised for compostible materials. Virtually anything of organic origins can be composted. Other materials can be saved that can be made into or used for something else, such as worn out clothes for rag rugs. Plastic bottles can be cut into tubes and recycled on the vegetable plot. They can protect delicate young plants from encroaching mulch or prevent collar rot on mulched trees when placed around the stems. They can also be cut into scoops, a funnel or a mini cloche for the garden. Heat from waste water can be recycled as can the water itself. Urine and excreta can be collected to contribute to the fertility of the soil. A good system for excreta is a pit privy.

We live in a consumer society but you do not have to contribute to the conspicuous consumption.

The Pit Privy

A simple way to deal with excreta is to have a pit privy and recycle your own waste. It is constructed of two cylinders part buried in the ground. These could be drainpipes or oil drums and require sealable lids. The one in use would require a hole in the lid, traditionally marked out for size using the foreman's bowler hat, and a flyproof vent to allow evaporation of moisture. Each time it is used a scoop of wood ash or sawdust should be put in.

Only human waste should go in. Collect urine in a separate container to go on a compost heap or to dilute with water and use as a general fertiliser. Once the pit is uncomfortably full, put the sealed lid on and leave for a year. It will then be a dark crumbly fertiliser ideal for fruit and other trees and flowers.

Figure 17: The Pit Privy

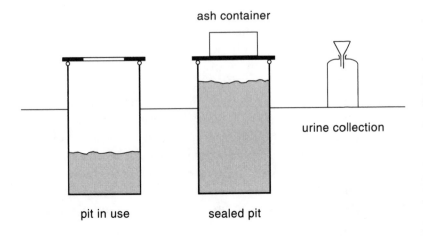

ash container

urine collection

pit in use   sealed pit

Domestic Rubbish Collection

Figure 18: Potential Domestic Rubbish Collection

Bins can be used for different categories of waste. One labelled 'waste' would be for things that cannot be used or recycled, such as plastics. The animal feed bin could be combined with the compost bin. They should be placed where they can be conveniently used, perhaps under the kitchen sink or outside the back door.

8

SHOPPING

What you buy, how you buy it and where you buy it are all things that need to be considered when rationalising your lifestyle. An awareness of what you are doing can be much more rewarding than working on impulse.

What You Buy

Buy basic ingredients, not processed food. Processed food often has many undesirable added ingredients, much superfluous packaging, is expensive and usually bland.

Consider all cleaning products as potential pollutants and see if there are any simpler alternatives.

Where possible buy goods that are produced locally, with minimum and recyclable packaging and are produced organically and ethically.

Try to avoid plastics and metals.

Try to buy seasonal, local produce and products made from natural materials.

How You Buy It

Keep a noticeboard so that things can be written down as they are running low. Try to cut down on shopping trips. This will involve some planning and probably the storage of staples. Possibly share shopping trips with others. Buying direct from suppliers, such as growers or wholesalers, can be combined with other people or trips for other purposes and will save money.

Where You Buy It

Buying from local producers is often cheaper, cuts down transportation and recycles your money within the community. Buying from local shops also helps to keep money within the community and promote local trade. National and multinational companies take money out of the community, require a vast, often global transportation system and consume enormous amounts of resources.

Manufactured Goods

Try to avoid buying disposable goods. Instead, buy durable, repairable, energy efficient, economical, local and ethically produced goods. Look for products made from renewable materials. It usually pays to buy good quality items. Local craftspeople often make beautiful durable products. Recycle by buying second-hand or refurbished items.

Local Trading

The benefits of local trading are not always immediately apparent.

Trading with local companies and with locally produced goods keeps the majority of cash spent circulating within the community. This is in contrast to trading with a national company where the majority of the cash spent goes out of the community.

The table on page 36 shows how money can be more efficiently recirculated within the community by trading locally. We take a token figure of 20% going out of the community in a local trading situation, and 20% staying in the community when trading with a national company. If we keep spending on the same basis, it can be seen that up to four times the money can be recirculated within the local community economy for its own benefit by spending it locally.

Figure 19: Local Trading Figures

LOCAL TRADING		NATIONAL TRADING	
In	Remaining	In	Remaining
10.00	8.00	10.00	2.00
8.00	6.40	2.00	0.40
6.40	5.12	0.40	0.08
5.12	4.10	0.08	0.02
4.10	3.28	0.02	
3.28	2.62	12.50	nil
2.62	2.10		
2.10	1.68		
1.68	1.34		
1.34	1.07		
1.07	0.86		
0.86	0.69		
0.69	0.55		
0.55	0.44		
0.44	0.35		
0.35	0.28		
0.28	0.22		
0.22	0.18		
0.18	0.14		
0.14	0.11		
0.11	0.09		
0.09	0.07		
0.07	0.06		
0.06	0.05		
0.05	0.04		
0.04	0.03		
0.03	0.02		
0.02	0.01		
0.01			
49.90	nil		

9

INPUTS & OUTPUTS

We, in the so called developed nations, consume up to three quarters of the world's resources. As individuals, collectively we can have a major impact, not only on ourselves and our community, but on the planet as a whole.

This is a listing of some of the things that come in and go out of a house. It is worth looking at each of these items to see where they come from, where we use them, where they end up, and how important they are to us. Do we really need them and if so what are viable alternatives and can we use less?

Whatever we use has some impact on the environment, but if what we do use comes from a renewable source and we use less, we are contributing towards a sustainable future.

Figure 20: House Inputs and Outputs
(see page 38)

IN	OUT	COMMENTS
People - residents, visitors, guests, social interaction	People - time; energy; information, food, CO_2, babies, noise	Use of time; importance of meeting spiritual, emotional; physical needs
Water - washing, watering, drink, sewage	Contaminated water, heat	Collecting rainwater, reclaiming heat, reusing water, chlorine, fluoride
Air - breathing, consumed by fires	Smoke, fumes, dust	Ventilating, draftproofing, not wasting heat
Energy - heating, power, lighting	Heat, gas, electromagnetic radiation	Cutting demand, reducing requirements
Food - people, animals, plants	Excreta, food waste, energy, heat, steam, dirty water, chemicals, packaging	Controlling production, putting excreta back on land
Drink	Urine, packaging, caffeine, gas, sugar	Collect urine as fertiliser
Clothes	Damaged or unfashionable	Recycle through charity shops or as rag rugs
Materials - cleaning, building, decorating	Toxic fumes, chemicals, poisons	Use natural non-toxic products
Equipment	Broken or outmoded, energy	Only necessary, low energy consumption; use rechargeable batteries
Furnishings	Non-degradable materials, toxic fumes	Use natural renewable, second hand
Books/magazines	Information, entertainment, waste paper, cash	Use library; only buy essentials
Post	Communication, waste paper	Stop circulars; reuse envelopes; paper; post cheaper than telephone
Information	Communication, interaction, sharing, meddling, helping	Do not hoard; exchange and share
Animals - companionship, therapy, food, fibre	Faeces, foodstuff, soiled bedding hair, dust, diseases	Pets consume vast quantities of high protein
Plants - materials, peat, compost	Oxygen, food, waste materials	Peat bogs being destroyed; many plants are plundered from wild
Packaging	Non-degradable oil based products	Waste in production; goes into landfills or is burnt
Chemicals - medicines, decorative, cleaning, insecticides	Pollution to us, the air, water and land	Medicines pollute black water

10

ALTERNATIVES
FOR USE IN THE HOUSE

There are many alternatives to the conventional, proprietary cleaners, potions and other items which are usually bought from shops. Try to obtain non-toxic solutions and do not just reach out to the nearest can or box available. Here are a few tips that may be useful.

Cleaning

All purpose | Many things can be cleaned with soapy water, left for a while to soak and then wiped off. Pure soap flakes or household soap will clean most things sometimes with a little washing soda if necessary.

Brass & copper | Mix white vinegar with baking soda to clean and polish brass and copper.

Burnt pans | Soak burnt pans overnight with salt or potato peelings, then bring to the boil.

Chrome | Use bicarbonate of soda to polish chrome.

Fridge | Wash out with bicarbonate of soda dissolved in water, then rinse with clean water.

Furniture | A cloth soaked in a solution of equal parts paraffin and vinegar then hung up to dry is good for polishing furniture. Keep in a sealed container.

Glass | Use vinegar and rinse with water to stop spotting.

Heat marks	Remove from stainless steel with a scourer and lemon juice.
House (general)	A house keeps much cleaner if shoes are taken off at the door.
Jewellery	Polish jewellery with a toothbrush and toothpaste.
Kettles	Descale kettles with white vinegar.
Narrow necked containers such as decanters	Use equal quantities of warm water, vinegar and sand.
Silver	Simmer for 10 minutes in water with aluminium foil or milk bottle tops and a tablespoon of washing soda.
Sinks & baths	Bicarbonate of soda makes a good scouring powder for sinks and baths. Sinks can also be cleaned and disinfected with salt. Coat the oven with it to make it easier to clean the next time.
Stale thermos	Can be freshened up with two teaspoons of bicarbonate of soda filled with boiling water and left overnight.
Toilet bowl	Leave white vinegar in overnight.
Washing powder	Use one cup of soap flakes and half cup of washing soda instead of washing powder. Prewash with washing soda to get rid of detergent residue which can go yellow.
Windows	Use a little vinegar in warm water and wipe with screwed up newspaper.

Stains

Ballpoint & felt tip ink	Use meths and then wash.
Blood	Soak in cold water.

Coffee & tea	Soak in one pint of warm water with one tablespoon of borax, then wash.
Fountain pen ink	Soak in milk before washing.
Fruit & beetroot	Pour hot water from a height immediately to force it out.
Grass	Rub with glycerine and leave for an hour before washing. Sponge cotton with methylated spirits and artificial fibres with equal parts meths and water.
Perspiration	Sponge with white vinegar or cover in bicarbonate of soda.
Tar	Eucalyptus oil or lighter fuel, or rub with lard then wash with washing soda.

Body

Bath perfume	Essential oils can be used to perfume the bath. Invigorating: 3 drops rosemary, 2 drops juniper. Sedative: 1 drop camomile, 4 drops lavender. Refreshing: juice from half lemon, 4 drops lemon oil, 1 drop geranium.
Deodorant	Bicarbonate of soda patted on or a few drops of rose or sandalwood essential oils mixed in a little vegetable oil.
Mouthwash	Use salty water.
Soap	Use oatmeal.
Lip moistener	Use almond oil.
Facial cleanser	Wash with milk rinsed with lukewarm water.

For a real treat with a friend if you have access to both a shower and a bath: Have a hot bath with herbs and oranges in it. Get out and rub each other's wet body with salt. Rinse off in the shower and get back in the bath. Get out and rub over with oatmeal. Rinse off and get back in the bath again. You and your skin will feel wonderful. This can be followed by a massage. Decorations, low lights, candles and music all add to the experience. Just the thing for a cold winter weekend.

Food

To keep tomato puree fresh in the fridge, cover with olive oil.

When garlic begins to sprout, trim and clean off cloves and cover in olive oil and keep in the fridge. The oil is delicious.

Keep an eating apple in the cake and bread tin to keep them moist.

Put a cube of sugar in the biscuit tin to keep them crisp.

Put a little rice in the salt pot to keep the salt dry.

Economies

Dilute washing up liquid with water.

Put a firebrick over a gas ring or pilot light for a prolonged low level heat source.

Put sticking plasters inside the finger ends of rubber gloves to make them last longer. When they are worn out cut them up for rubber bands or use to keep a car distributor dry.

Cotton wool will swell to twice its size if it is unfolded and put in an airing cupboard.

A hot water bottle will last longer if a few drops of glycerine are put in the first time it is used.

A natural sponge can be restored if it is soaked overnight in a warm solution of washing soda then washed in soapy water.

Odd ends of soap can be put in a small container with a few drops of glycerine, put into boiling water until softened. Then mould into a new tablet by hand. Alternatively, put a little boiling water over the slivers and you will have a soap jelly for washing dishes, for the shower or for diluting to spray greenfly.

Others

Make scourers with nylon mesh bags stuffed inside each other and tied up.

Keep the thawed ice from the fridge or freezer as it is distilled water. Use in steam iron and car batteries.

A stiff zip can be made to run freer if a lead pencil is rubbed on it.

42

A stiff lock can sometimes be freed by running a pencil on the key.

Talc on a curtain track makes it run easier.

Strain paints or jellies through an old pair of tights or stockings.

To dry the insides of wet shoes or boots stuff with newspaper.

Stop yellowing of white cottons and linens by wrapping in blue tissue and store away from strong light.

Mothproof by putting dried orange peel amongst clothes or use sachets of cinnamon, cloves, black pepper and orris root, or use lavender.

Drains blocked with grease can be cleared with washing soda.

The smell of tobacco smoke can be cleared by placing a bowl of cider vinegar in a room overnight.

Deter mice by using tansy and mint.

Deter ants from cupboards by using rue, tansy or penny royal.

Get rid of ants by putting down a mixture of borax and icing sugar.

Control of
Your Food

11

WE ARE WHAT WE EAT!

We are what we eat. If so, what are we now? We know that some things will be harmful to us if we eat them, such as arsenic or washing up liquid. Some things are quite possibly dangerous to eat but we do not know yet what effects they may have. Some things are in our food but we do not even know they are there, let alone what they do. We can only control what is in our food if we know what is in it, the purpose of any additive's presence and in what way it may be dangerous.

Why Are Additives Dangerous?

Great Britain has one of the highest incidence of cardiovascular diseases in the world. This means that we are prone to heart attacks, strokes, angina and limb problems that can often lead to amputation. These, of course, can be caused by smoking, but also by some of the following:

Salt

An excess leads to hypertension and high blood pressure.

Sugar

Sugar increases weight, which increases blood pressure, cholesterol and the danger of diabetes.

Fats

Saturated fats increase weight and cholesterol levels which block arteries.

Processed Food

The majority of processed foods include saturated fats, sugar, modified starches as well as a large number of additives.

Why Additives Are Added

The primary motive for manufacturers including additives in their products is to increase profit. The effects that food additives have on the consumer seem to be of secondary concern. Cheaper, inferior products such as saturated fats, sugars, modified starches and water are substituted for superior, more expensive products.

Flavourings and deodorisers are then added to disguise the taste and smell of these inferior products. The shelf life is prolonged by using deoxidants, saturated fats and preservatives to make us think that it is fresh. Emulsifiers and dyes are added to improve appearance and various chemicals are added to increase the speed and efficiency of processing.

How Foods Are Processed

Meat Products

Cooked Meats

Cooked meat products such as pies contain a high level of saturated fat and can include the following that are not defined as meat: brains, feet, intestines, lungs, oesophagus, rectum, spinal cord, spleen, testicles and udder.

Cured Meat

Cured meats contain polyphosphates (E450). The meat is massaged or beaten to increase the amount of water it retains. It also contains nitrates to maintain the pink colour. Nitrates combine with haemoglobin to stop the blood carrying oxygen and with amines to form carcinogenic nitrosamines in the body.

Poultry

Poultry is repeatedly washed, soaked and treated with polyphosphates to increase the amount of water absorbed.

Sausages

A beef sausage needs to contain 50% meat and half of this must be lean. The 'lean' portion can be fat, gristle, sinews, head meat, heart, kidney, liver, pancreas, tail meat, thymus, tongue and gizzard. The other 50% is usually fat, cereal and water. Sausages can also include polyphosphates to enhance water retention and colour, flavour enhancers to disguise taste and hide blandness, antioxidants and preservatives.

Fish Products

Battered Fish

This is often made from a moulded paste like fish fingers. Many such products have been shown to have 34% fish, 10% water and, of course, batter.

Fish Fingers

A lot of fish is sold as fish fingers. These are cut from fish blocks which can comprise filleted fish, fish mince (bones, entrails, blood and other waste), polyphosphates and water. Many of the cheaper fish fingers are cut thinner and covered with a thicker coating of batter and breadcrumbs, of which the yellow colour is often azo.

Prawns

Prawns (likewise fish) are often sold with a glaze of water. This is yet another example of the processor getting a good price for water!

Scampi

Much of the scampi we eat is an extruded paste which has to include at least 50% scampi. This 50% can also contain water.

Other Food Products

Beer

Dimethylpolysiloxane is used as a foam control agent in the brewing process. This can contain formaldehyde as a contaminant and both substances are suspected to be carcinogenic. Ammonium caramel is used as a colouring agent even though it can produce blood disorders. Alginate esters are used to produce more head when too little malt is used. One of them, called gum acacia, is used to maintain a head and has been linked to hypersensitivity. Bleach (potassium bromide) is used in the early stages of brewing to speed up fermentation and can cause stomach and bowel disorders. Sulphur dioxide is used to preserve weak beer. Because malt is replaced by cheaper substitutes like sugar, flour or potato starch, many beers lack body and taste.

Biscuits

These are mainly cream, saturated fats, sugars, chocolate, refined flour, salt, artificial flavourings and colourings. Also included are the usual antioxidants, preservatives, improvers and stabilisers. Many manufacturers use patent flours, 40% of which are pure wheat starch. Fats account for up to one third of the weight of biscuits and are usually saturated or hardened. Sugars can constitute up to half the weight and comprise sucrose, fructose, maltrose, dextrose, glucose or syrups.

Bread

White and brown bread are refined to a point where they contain very few vitamins, fibre or minerals. They are mixed at high speed with water, yeast, sugar, fat, salt, yeast nutrients, chemical improvers and other chemicals which do away with the need for long fermentation but also with the flavour. Flour improvers, which include bleach, are used to make a stronger dough which retains more water and gas. These can include up to 30 additives, including caramel.

Chutneys, Sauces and Ketchups

Most have large quantities of sugar, salt and modified starches which thicken to allow the addition of more water.

Fruit and Vegetables

Fruit and vegetables are frequently tired and old by the time they reach the shopping basket. Most are doused with a cocktail of fertilisers, herbicides, pesticides and fungicides which coat them and are absorbed during growth. Many are gassed, sprayed with fungicides and growth inhibitors to control ripening and to allow long periods of storage. Many come from countries that use chemicals that even the English ban. The national habit of overboiling in salted water also destroys and leaches out many of the nutrients. The water that is used for cooking is often more nutritious!

Ice Cream

Ice cream is usually made from low grade vegetable oils which are modified with chemical emulsifiers, stabilisers and chemical flavourings. The colourings used are often tartrazine (E102), sunset yellow (E110), and amaranth (E123). All of these are azo dyes which cause hyperactivity in children.

Jams

Most commercial products have large amounts of sugar and azo dyes.

Margarine

'High in polyunsaturates' means that the product usually contains more than 45% in content. Cheap oils are used unless specified otherwise. Vegetable oils can be saturated or hydrogenised to make them harder. Deodorisers are used with some oils, such as fish, to make them more palatable. Oil is emulsified with up to 26% of water and emulsifying agents added to stop separation. Cheaper oils are often saturated and usually also contain 2% salt. Low fat spreads are margarine with more water added and a gelatine to make them firm.

Soft Cheeses

Many soft cheeses contain emulsifiers and stabilisers to stop separation.

Soft Drinks

Soft drinks usually consist of water, sugar, colourings, flavourings and fizz. Any real fruit juice contained may be in minute quantities only.

What Can You Do?

We can eat as little processed food as possible and be more discerning about what we buy. We can also read the labels to check what is in the food. We can control what we eat by producing our own food from basic ingredients which we can more easily ensure are uncontaminated. Limit cholesterol intake by frying less and consuming less red meat, offal, dairy produce and eggs. Eat more fatty fish as it has been shown to reduce cholesterol. Buy organic and wholefoods. Bake your own bread, cakes and biscuits using oil and sweeten with dried fruit. The best oils are sunflower, safflower and olive as they do not contribute to cholesterol. Eat more raw or steamed vegetables as less nutrients are lost. Eat locally produced seasonal products where possible.

12

WHAT YOU CAN DO

You can gain greater control of your food by buying it direct from the producer and/or banding together with others to purchase in bulk, or better still, by controlling its production and growing it yourself.

Self Growing

We can all grow something for ourselves. There is always space for something in the kitchen, on windowsills, on a balcony or roof, in containers, on walls, in a yard, a greenhouse or in the garden. If you do not have enough space for your needs or any space at all, there are alternatives to having your own garden. There might be gardens or greenhouses nearby that are not being used. Their owners might be pleased for you to use these in exchange for some of the produce. There are usually allotments available. There is often derelict or unused land around that you might obtain permission to use as a community garden, an orchard or as a city farm or permaculture demonstration site. Try approaching the local council, public utilities, local industries or businesses. Community projects are being increasingly encouraged by official bodies, especially if they are self sustaining. Local schools or community centres might have areas available as well.

Control

You can barter for food with local producers such as allotment holders, city farms or organic growers. They can all be part of a LETSystem *(see page 54)*. There are also a number of working examples of Community Supported Agriculture (CSA). These are schemes where the producer is paid a set sum in advance and the consumer receives a proportion of the produce. The consumer also usually has some say in what is grown.

There are examples of CSAs providing organic vegetables and fruit, free range eggs and even shares in a cow so that the 'owners' can drink their own untreated milk. Each scheme varies, but most involve a set fee being paid at the beginning of the season to share the risk with the producer and also any bonanza. The fee can be adjusted if the consumer contributes some work, such as cultivation, harvesting or delivery.

CSA is an efficient method for bringing organic produce into cities. Farms, or their co-operatives, usually bring their produce to a collecting point (e.g. someone's house) from where it is locally redistributed. This cuts out the supermarket chains and their massive inherent costs (e.g. for packing, transport and marketing), it supports the smaller organic farmer (giving greater independence from the dictates of the supermarkets) and gives a regular supply of fresh, high quality organic food virtually direct to the consumer. This is a true consumer created market.

Buying

Bulk buying will reduce costs and can directly influence suppliers if the demand is large enough. You could undertake a regular trip to the wholesale organic market or wholefood warehouse. Your surplus produce could also be sold there at the same time to reduce your costs. You can join together with friends to increase the quantities you purchase and therefore lower the costs. It might be possible to work with another group that already buy in bulk or purchases wholesale, such as food co-ops, self sufficiency groups, Henry Doubleday Research Association (HDRA), the Soil Association or Friends of the Earth (FoE) groups. In Japan, large domestic purchasing groups have the power to dictate their requirements to the manufacturers and suppliers.

13

LIVING ABUNDANTLY WITH LESS MONEY

LETS stands for Local Exchange Trading System. It is an extended barter system of which there are now many successful working examples throughout the world.

LETS has an advantage over barter in that an individual (or business) is not limited to an exchange directly with just one other person. It frees everyone to trade within the local economy, and therefore also empowers people who have skills and resources (such as time, for instance), but not necessarily money. LETS works entirely within the law and takes into account government agencies such as Social Security and the Inland Revenue.

How LETS Works

A start up group sets an exchange unit which is approximately equivalent to one pound, dollar, an hours labour or whatever. A list of services and goods offered or required is then circulated to the group. Offers and requests can be for anything: from foodstuffs, baby-sitting or manual labour, to car maintenance, printing or dental treatment! The more members that join, the more diverse the goods and services available become. To trade, one person contacts someone on the list who has what is required. A price for the trade is then agreed which can be entirely in LETS units or in a percentage of LETS units and cash (materials and expenses are often paid for in cash). There is a central register where each transaction, in the form of a cheque, is recorded as a debit and credit to each account as appropriate. There are now low cost software packages available for personal computers that make this accounting system easy.

Each party is clearly accountable. As the account records are open, it is easy to check on who is trading and to what extent. Because LETS is always locally based, experience shows that the system is not abused.

Being a member of a LETSystem is a very good way to meet a variety of local people!

Using What You've Got

14

WITHOUT A GARDEN

Even if you do not have a garden, it is still possible to grow a variety of things to eat. It is possible to grow edible plants in window boxes, pots of herbs and smaller plants on windowsills and germinate shoots and sprouts in jars. You can even grow mushrooms in cupboards.

Window boxes need to be fixed securely and in a position where they can be reached and do not interfere with the opening window. If it is not possible to fix them to the wall, it might be possible to hang them from the window. Window boxes can also be fixed to the inside as well as the outside. They can be planted with all the plants that are usually grown outside such as herbs, salads, nasturtiums, strawberries, french beans or small tomatoes. Hanging baskets can perform the same function.

Plants that can be grown in pots or in interior plant troughs include herbs, such as parsley, mint, chives or thyme, but one of the best is sweet basil. A number of salad plants can be grown, especially in the winter, such as American cress, rocket, the mustards and some lettuces. Other possible plants to include are the more tender ones such as tomatoes, aubergines, peppers and chillies.

It might also be possible to build a small greenhouse outside the window to extend the growing season, grow plants in winter, provide insulation and to serve the purpose of a greenhouse for tender plants.

Sprouted seeds can give you all year round fresh and healthy food. One of the simplest ways of growing them is to do what you probably did when you were a kid. Put a thin layer of absorbent material, such as tissues or a piece of fabric, in a shallow container.

Ensure that the seeds have not been dressed with poisons for planting. Seeds should be soaked overnight, then spread over the moist base. Keep the base moist and cover until sprouting. Then harvest when they have reached a few inches. Suitable seeds are mung, lentil, mustard, cress, radish, rape, coriander, alfalfa or fenugreek.

Another method is to soak them overnight, then rinse twice daily and keep at a reasonable temperature. I use a plastic container with a piece of net curtain over the top held on with an elastic band and keep them in the airing cupboard. They are usually ready in about three to four days, depending on temperature and age of seeds. Probably the best source for some of these organic seeds is from a health food shop with a quick turnover. Seeds that are suitable include mung, adzuki, lentil, alfalfa, fenugreek, radish, wheat, rye, barley and triticale. Sprouts will grow fat and long if grown under pressure. One way is to place a polythene bag filled with water on the top of them.

Mushroom growing kits can be bought as a prepared box which can give quite a good yield. These can be grown under a sink, in a cupboard, in a cellar or in a garage. Try to get one with an organic base.

Figure 21: Window Greenhouse

glazing around window

plants on shelves

bracket

Figure 22: Growing at a Window

15

BALCONIES

Dependent on the size, a balcony has potential for the production of many different kinds of foodstuffs. Trellising up the walls, not only on the balcony, but also on the flanking walls can support container grown plants. Containers on the floor, the walls and suspended from the ceiling, as well as the railings, can give a substantial growing area. Logs can supply edible fungi and rabbits and quail can be kept in hutches.

Figure 23: Growing on a Balcony
(see page 62)

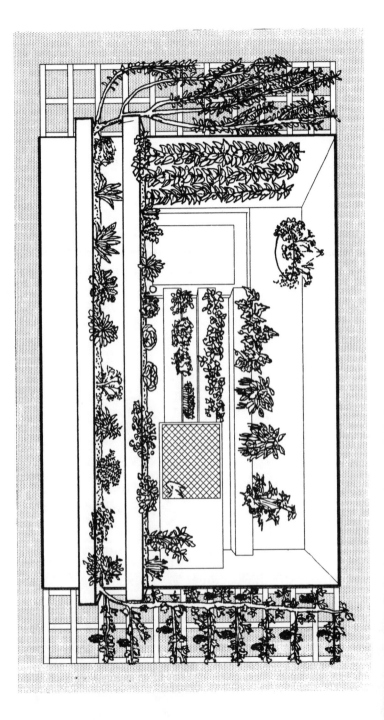

Figure 23: Growing on a Balcony

16

VERTICAL SURFACES

Vertical surfaces have great potential for growing plants. If the surfaces are south facing, they can heat up during the day to promote growth early and late in the season. In a small area, this can often conflict with the desire to leave it bare and paint it white to reflect more light into the area as a whole. Planting, however, can do more than provide a crop. A conservatory or glazed door can benefit in the summer by being shaded with a deciduous vine or climbing plant growing over it. Evergreen foliage on walls also acts as an insulator in winter.

Climbing Annuals

If a trellis, net or wires are securely fixed a few inches away from the wall, the following plants will climb, given the right soil and weather conditions:

Asparagus pea
> Very decorative and prolific. The main problem is picking them fast enough!

Climbing french beans
> Can be very prolific and very tasty. They have the additional advantage that they can be left to dry on the vine for haricot beans.

Cucumbers and gherkins
> These will climb up most things.

Melons
> These are worth trying in the warmer microclimate of a town.

Nasturtium

> The flowers and leaves can be eaten in salads and have a pleasant peppery taste. (The leaves are wonderful in a cheese sandwich.) The seed pods can be popped into spiced vinegar as a substitute for capers.

Peas

> I do not like discarding the shells and so I have always grown sugar snap or mangetout peas as you can eat everything.

Runner beans

> The most common variety of bean which is also very decorative.

Winter squash

> Will climb all over a hedge or fence and give a good crop of delicious squashes which may keep until early spring.

Climbing Perennials

Most need training or tying back:

Berries

> There are a great variety of these. Most need training and last year's fruiting growth cut out. Thornless varieties are available. Most will grow in semi-shaded positions. Remontant strawberries taste like alpine strawberries and can climb up to two metres. They will crop from early August until November.

Grape

> Can be trained up a wall or over beams above head height. Some of the American grapes are useful.

Honeysuckle

> *Lonicera edulis caerulea.* A variety with edible berries.

Kiwi Fruit

> *Actinidia kolomikta.* A good variety for smaller gardens. Others are more vigorous. Needs one male plant to every three females for pollination.

Top fruit

> Most top fruits can be trained up walls, either cordoned, espaliered or fan trained. Choose varieties that are self pollinating or that are in the same flowering period.

There are also 'family' trees that have more than one variety grafted onto the same root stock, useful when space is limited. Morello cherries will flourish on a north facing wall where most other fruits will not. Try peaches or nectarines on a south facing sheltered wall. For more varieties, check a good fruit grower's guide or a specialist nursery's catalogue. Unusual varieties are supplied by Clive Simms and Future Foods.

Figure 24: Using a Vertical Surface

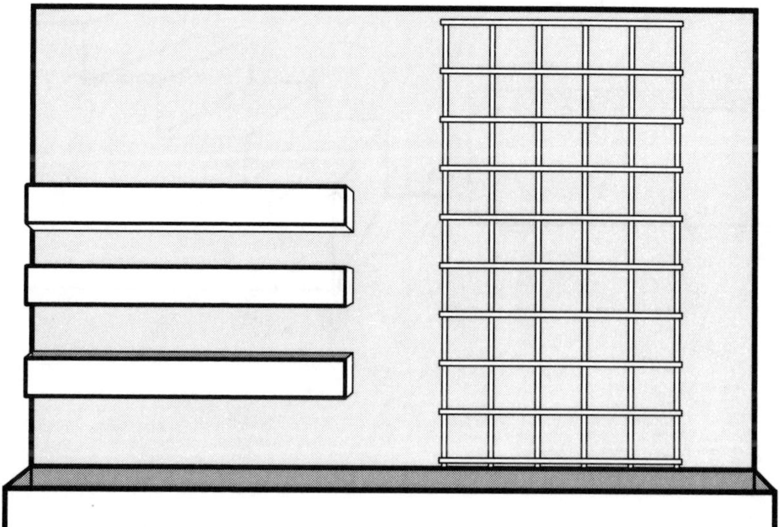

Stepped Containers

A series of plant troughs or containers can be fixed up a wall, or on shelves, and can be stepped to allow access and light. These can be planted with virtually anything: herbs, salad greens and hanging plants such as tomatoes or strawberries will all work especially well in such a situation. The small currant variety of tomatoes are prolific and delicious.

Figure 25: Stepped Containers

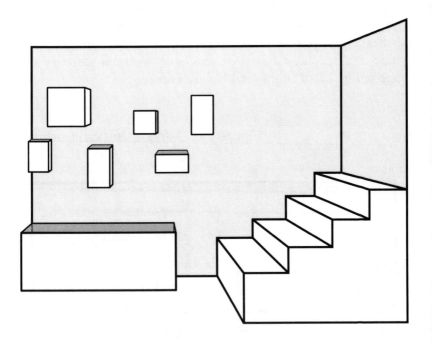

17

NEAR THE ROADSIDE

A garden near a road is vulnerable to pollution from heavy metals such as lead or cadmium. A first line of defence to stop pollution is a barrier such as a hedge. Leafy plants have been shown to absorb more heavy metals than root crops or fruits. Food crops should not be closer than 7.5 metres from the road. If it is essential to grow foodstuffs near a road, they should be washed with a 1% solution of vinegar.

Other uses for a garden near a road could be for growing nuts, fruits, sunflowers, Jerusalem artichoke or grains for livestock feed. Plants with other uses can also be grown, such as bamboo for garden stakes or a variety of plants such as willows, rushes, sedges or reeds for basketry.

Plants for Basketry

Dogwood, *Cornus sanguinea.* Green and red stems.
Osier, *Salix viminalis.*
Purple willow, *Salix purpurea.* For fine basket work.
Violet willow, *Salix daphnoides.* Has dark purple stems.

18

SMALL GARDENS

A small area has the potential for very high productivity as you are able to concentrate more on focusing on detail. In a very small area I would recommend concentrating on high yielding, high value plants and varieties which yield fruit that are particularly important to eat as fresh as possible. A small area will usually have a number of vertical surfaces which can be exploited. Plantings can supply salad plants, herbs, soft fruit, vines, beans and peas, courgettes and winter squashes.

Stacked logs can yield crops of edible fungi.

A stack of tyres filled with compost can yield a good crop of salad potatoes.

Quail, rabbits and perhaps a small dovecote can be kept within a small area. Trimmings and surpluses from the garden could supplement their feed. The manure and waste from the houses can provide fertility to the soil directly or by way of the compost or worm bin.

A small greenhouse or glass frame can be heated by a water tank that uses the grey water from the bath or basin before going down the drain. A high level rainwater collection tank can have a tap that is permanently piped to containers and plantings to give a drip feed when turned on. A secondary tank underneath can take the overflow which would supply even more water.

Figure 26: Small Garden Plan

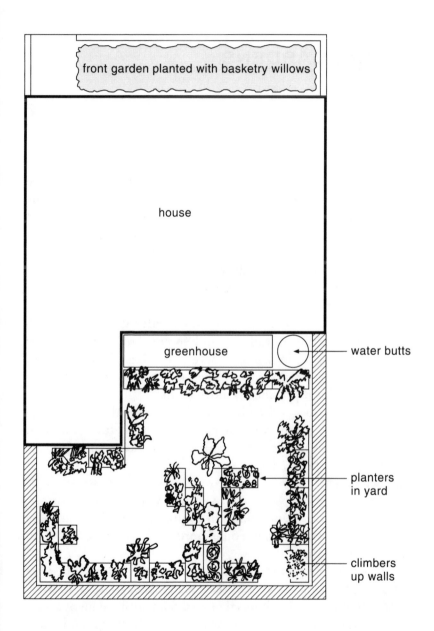

front garden planted with basketry willows

house

greenhouse

water butts

planters in yard

climbers up walls

19

LARGE GARDENS

When preparing your plan of action, the first thing you need to assess is what already exists in your garden. Then consider all the things that you need to have in the garden. Finally, decide on what you would like to have in the garden and how it will be used.

When assessing what you already have, list the existing plants and trees. How useful and attractive are they? Can they be transplanted or must they remain in position? What is the orientation of the garden? Which areas get the most sunlight and which are the most shaded? Is the site windy? If so, from which direction does the prevailing wind come? Are there any frost pockets? What buildings are there? (This can include sheds, greenhouses or workshops.) What is the condition of these buildings and is it possible to move them?

What do you need to have and what would you like to have in your garden? Consider, for instances: food, animals, compost heap, watering system, storage, greenhouse/conservatory, wildlife area, pond, clothes line, sitting and play space or barbecue area?

What plants do you want to grow? What are the sources, special requirements, planting and cropping times? Are you going to include a forest garden, edible borders, keyhole beds, a herb spiral or all of these?

Once you have chosen the elements you wish to include, you can start to design on paper. A scale plan is always useful to work to. Try to position the things that you need most frequent access to near the back door. This would include herbs and salad vegetables. A very important and early step in the design process is to decide on the circulation - the pathways round the garden and access to different areas.

Multiple Functions

Try to combine elements to give them as many functions as possible. Grow vines around and over rainwater storage tanks with a dovecote on top to provide a ready supply of manure.

A combined chicken house and greenhouse *(see page 122)* will provide heat from the chickens in winter and at night and a ready supply of manure. Annual climbers over the greenhouse/chicken house will provide shade in the summer but not restrict light in the winter. A rainwater storage tank collecting from the roof of the greenhouse/chicken house could be positioned next to the vegetable plot and trimmings from the vegetable plot can be thrown into the chicken run. Also, position the greenhouse so that it is in the shade of a house or tree in the hottest part of the summer day. A deciduous tree is best as it admits sunlight in the winter and provides shading in the summer when it is needed.

Rabbits can be housed over part of the chicken run so that any debris can be eaten by the chickens as well as any flies attracted by the manure.

Bees can be positioned behind a hedge which pushes their flight path up overhead. Fruiting and bee forage varieties can be chosen for the hedge. Bee hives can be positioned on the edge of a pond so that they are near water, and dead bees cleared out of the hive are food for the fish. The pond can be placed in front of the conservatory to reflect winter sunlight.

How are you going to water the garden? Perhaps from the mains, with rainwater collection, grey water or a combination of these? How are you going to distribute the water? Through hoses, sprinklers, trickle hoses or underground? Commercial trickle hoses work well. They can be connected to your water source and turned on when needed, thus freeing you to do other things. They deliver water just where it is needed and therefore do not waste water.

Figure 27: Large Garden Plan

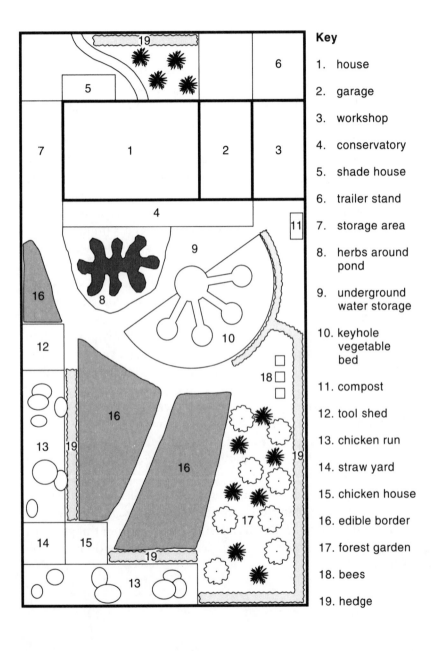

Key

1. house
2. garage
3. workshop
4. conservatory
5. shade house
6. trailer stand
7. storage area
8. herbs around pond
9. underground water storage
10. keyhole vegetable bed
11. compost
12. tool shed
13. chicken run
14. straw yard
15. chicken house
16. edible border
17. forest garden
18. bees
19. hedge

Creating Your Own Food Supply

20

WHAT TO GROW

What to grow is determined by a number of factors. What size area do you have? How much light is available? (A minimum of about six hours is needed.) What is the condition of the soil. What plants do you like best? Do you want to grow herbs, vegetables, salad, fruit, fungi, craft materials, bee forage, biomass, dyeing or medicinal plants. Of course, your own resources such as cash, time, space and fitness are also determining factors.

People grow their plants for a variety of reasons; to save money, to have fresh food, to eat produce that is not available in the shops, to ensure that their food intake is organic, for pleasure, for aesthetics and to connect with the soil and nature. To this can be added that they are taking some responsibility for food production and in so doing are giving themselves more control over the food that they eat.

Varieties

Many varieties are not commercially available. The normal produce available in shops is selected for appearance, the ability to travel, to be even sized, for maximum yield, to be ready at the same time, to ripen after picking and, all too often, to respond well to chemicals. When you grow your own food, you can select different criteria such as flavour, disease resistance, cropping over a long period, ability to stand in the ground for a long period of time, good when eaten raw or not normally available.

Fruit

There is an enormous variety of fruit available. Visit places like RHS Brogdale or Wisley to see what they are like. Select varieties that give you fresh fruit over the longest period possible and ensure that if they are not self pollinators that they have the correct pollinators near by. There are some varieties that are superb for jams or bottling. Numerous varieties are not readily available such as medlars, quince, tayberry, cape gooseberry to mention a few. There are a large number of edible decorative plants as listed in the edible garden section.

Vegetables

There are a large variety of vegetables available, perennial as well as annual. There are now many oriental varieties on the market that grow in cold conditions and will extend your range.

Herbs will often supplement salads and are companion plants to many species, having a beneficial relationship with them.

21

COMPOST

Compost is very useful in a garden. It adds nutrients, fibrous matter and minerals to the soil. It improves the soil structure and moisture retention in open soils if added as a mulch when the soil is already moist. It is usually best added to the soil as a top covering of mulch where the worms will carry it into the soil rather than digging it in. There is not usually enough waste matter to fill a standard compost bin in the average household unless one collects organic materials from outside, such as from verges, unused allotments, greengrocers, trimmings and clearings from pet hutches or stables. An alternative is to have group compost bins between about six families.

Two other alternatives are a rotating bin or a worm bin. Both can be purchased but are quite easy to make. A rotating bin is a plastic container with a large lid clamped to the top. It is supported in the centre so that it can be rotated. Raw waste is put in and the bin is turned over every day. The compost is ready in just a few weeks.

A worm bin consists of a plastic container with a lid. There are holes drilled around at about 75mm from the bottom. Put gravel in the bottom up to the holes and then add water until it comes out of the holes. Put in a few inches of vegetable matter mixed with a little manure and a small handful of calcified seaweed to maintain the pH level. Add some brandlings (tiger worms), which are small red worms that can be found in compost or obtained from any angling shop, then add vegetable matter as it becomes available. Also add crushed eggshells to keep the pH level in balance. At regular intervals take out the worm caste, which is very rich, and give the surplus worms to the chickens or sell them back to the angling shop. Keep the bin in a sheltered place in cold weather as the worms become inactive when cold.

Another good way to compost is to put all your waste on the floor of a chicken house. If you throw a few handfuls of feed on the floor every day as well, the chickens will turn it and you will have enriched compost ready to put on the soil in a few weeks in the summer.

A shredder is very useful for chopping up all those things that take too long to rot and are normally burnt, such as prunings from hedges, fruit trees, roses, soft fruit, maize, artichoke stems or brassica stalks. It is quite an investment and only used occasionally, so it would be useful to purchase one between a group of people.

What Can You Put in the Compost?

Virtually anything of organic origins can be added to the compost heap. This could be kitchen waste, lawn mowings, vegetable trimmings, clearings from animal houses, weeds, shredded twigs, manure and leaves.

Figure 28: Worm Bin

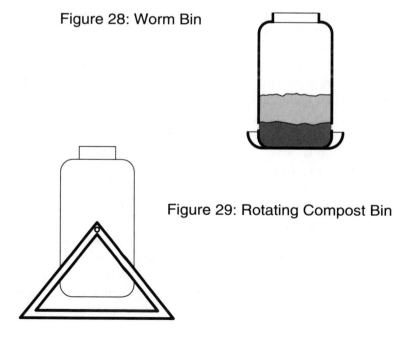

Figure 29: Rotating Compost Bin

22

MULCHING

Nature does not like bare soil. If it is left bare something will grow, or the surface will compact and form a crust, or alternatively erosion will occur.

Mulching has many functions. It is used to suppress weed growth, provide nutrients to the soil, conserve moisture, allow easy removal of weeds growing in it, to stop surface compaction and the formation of a crust, prevent erosion, to stop the surface overheating and to clear new sites.

Mulching will clear the soil of weeds without disturbing the structure. Most people dig the soil, but this actually destroys its structure. Good soil structure is necessary for worm movement, which allows air, moisture and roots to penetrate the soil. Digging also destroys the living top few inches of the soil with its myriad of micro-organisms that then have to re-establish themselves. It is better to hoe and mulch.

If an area is clear and you are not ready to plant, do not leave it bare, but grow a green manure crop or mulch over it. A good manure crop is clover as it puts nitrogen back into the soil. Any subsequent planting can be in this. Other green manures are alfalfa, buckwheat, lupins, mustard and Hungarian grazing rye.

Compost too is a good mulch as it adds nutrient to the soil as well as organic matter.

Lawn mowings make a good mulch as they form a solid mat. Mowings will suppress weed growth, and are particularly useful around crops such as soft fruit and nitrogen fixers like beans, as the need to hoe would otherwise disturb their shallow roots. Mowings can also be used as a path mulch.

Straw is also useful for keeping the cold off root vegetables and off delicate plants. Ensure that a straw inhibitor has not been sprayed on as this inhibits the growth of your plants just as it does the straw length.

Leaf mould made by piling leaves in a wire cage for a year or two and kept moist makes a useful mulch.

Sawdust or wood shavings can cause nitrogen depletion, so only use them on paths. Sawdust can be piled and rotted before putting on the garden or used in animal housing. The addition of urine will help to speed up the composting process. Use sawdust from sources where preservatives and insecticides have not been used.

Black polythene held down on the ground over winter will clear the soil of grass and weeds. The soil will be covered with worm castes when the plastic is lifted in the spring and you will have a ready made tilth for planting. To kill off any remaining perennial weeds, keep the polythene in place for the first year and simply plant through small cut holes.

Carpets make a good temporary ground cover. As carpets tend to rot, use those made from natural fibres as nylon or polypropalene getting into the soil is not a good idea.

A living mulch of close growing plants will suppress weed growth and can provide protection for delicate plants.

Sheet mulch is best for clearing lawn or rough ground. This uses a large quantity of materials that have to be collected first but is very effective. To prepare the area to be mulched, first cut down any tall growth. Soak the area with water before covering or, better still, mulch it after heavy rain. Scatter calcified seaweed over the site (about half a baked bean tin per square metre). Cover the area with about 10 to 15 cm of organic material. There should be a thin layer of manure, so add leaves, stable clearings, grass mowings, shreddings, spoilt hay and virtually anything that will compost. Pour over urine that you have collected and diluted one part urine to ten parts water. Over this put a layer of newspaper (a newspaper opened out is about the right thickness) or flattened cardboard boxes. Soak these well and then cover with a layer of weed free mulch, such as grass mowings, straw, leaf mould, sawdust, woodchips or seaweed. Cut through this and plant in the soil below or, for potatoes, simply place on top of the soil within the mulch.

23

CONTAINER GARDENING

Container growing is suitable in small patio gardens, on roofs, balconies and for delicate plants. This form of growing has the advantage that you can adapt the soil to the plants if they have special requirements. Also, your carefully made compost or worm caste can be used to its maximum advantage as it is contained within the areas needed. Delicate plants can be grown in containers which have the advantage that they can be moved into the shelter in cold weather. An alternative is to make tailor-made cloches which can be brought out when required. If frames are made to fit the containers, then either glazed or covered in polythene to make cold frames, cropping time can be extended by starting early and growing later in the season. They will also protect salads which will flourish over winter.

Types of Containers

Containers can take any form that you can imagine. Virtually any durable container will do. Potential containers, that you can often find thrown away and/or acquire for free, could include buckets, baths, basins, barrels (wood, plastic or metal), water tanks, chimney pots, packing cases, tyres (either stacked or cut round on a hub) or lined mesh containers. Hanging baskets are particularly useful.

Home-made containers can be constructed of timber, brick or ferro cement. If making portable containers yourself, it makes rearrangement easier if they are all built to a module so they can be stacked or meshed together. One size cloche would also fit all of them.

Timber containers can be constructed on heavy castors for moving about on a yard or patio. Lining with plastic will reduce rotting but make holes in the bottom to allow drainage. Heavy duty shuttering ply is available from building sites and does not rot. Alternatively sleepers can be used and spiked together.

Ferro cement is a form of construction that uses a frame of metal rods which is covered in a number of layers of mesh, and cement is then pushed into the mesh. It is used to make boats and water tanks, so it is very strong.

Bought containers are usually very expensive, although strawberry pots are fun and can be used to grow other things such as herbs. A common type of container is the growbag. After a crop you can reuse the compost in other containers and refill the growbags with fresh compost. You can, however, simply make your own growbags by filling plastic sacks with compost.

Containers usually have drainage holes at the bottom. These are then covered with broken pots or tiles to assist drainage and filled with a moisture retaining potting compost. This is regularly topped with a mulch to continue enriching the soil, to stop evaporation and to smother weeds. Due to the danger of drying out in the summer, a permanent trickle feed installed to maintain the moisture level is desirable, otherwise they will have to be watered on most days.

Potting Compost

Potting compost is expensive and is often peat based. If you have to buy it, try one that is based on some other material. You can make your own potting compost by mixing seven parts soil with three parts peat substitute, such as leaf mould, two parts sharp sand and a quarter part calcified seaweed. This should be sieved and thoroughly mixed with approximately two parts of well rotted manure or compost.

Other methods of filling your containers:

1) Fill them with last year's leaves well soaked and top up with five to ten centimetres of soil or compost. As the level sinks, top up with home made compost.

2) Use a bale of well soaked hay, either wrap in plastic or in a container to stop evaporation. Spoilt hay can sometimes be

81

acquired for nothing. Make holes in it to hold pockets of soil or cover it in a layer of soil or compost. One or a half bale size could be the basis for your planting module sizes. This method can be used on top of the soil in a garden, adding organic matter to the soil as it rots down.

What to Plant

Fruit trees can be grown in containers, preferably on dwarfing rootstock and with suitable pollinators. They can be free standing or trained up walls or a trellis. In a sun trap against a wall, delicate top fruit such as apricots or nectarines can be grown. Soft fruits can be grown in most positions as they can crop in shaded positions. A particularly good fruit for a shaded area is sour cherry. A bay tree makes a good container grown subject and can be surrounded by a range of herbs, salads or maybe alpine strawberries.

Most vegetables can be grown in containers. The decorative cabbages and kales taste and look good. Tomatoes and basil sown together make a good summer crop. If you wish to grow early or a special variety of potato (such as pink fir apples), plant about five tubers in the ground inside a tyre and put a piece of glass over them to protect when planting early. As the foliage grows, top up with soil or compost and keep adding tyres and compost until cropping. Ensure that they have enough water and you will get a large crop from a small area.

Figure 30: Sleepers Spiked Together

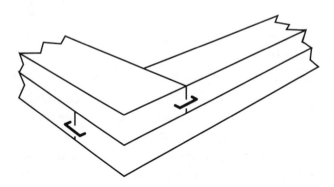

Figure 31: Hay Bale Container

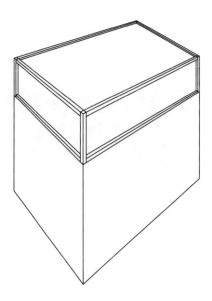

Figure 32: Section Through Hay Bale Container

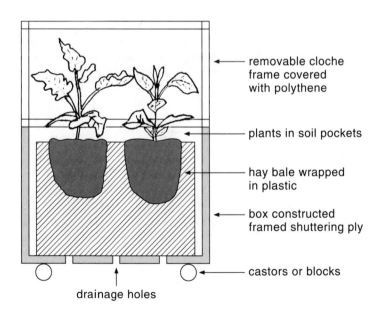

removable cloche
frame covered
with polythene

plants in soil pockets

hay bale wrapped
in plastic

box constructed
framed shuttering ply

castors or blocks

drainage holes

Figure 33: Tyre Planter

cut around
tyre on
wheel hub

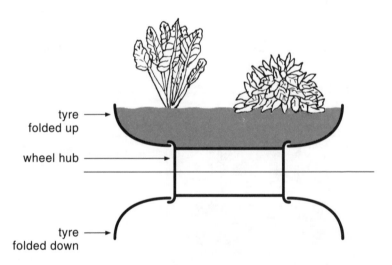

tyre
folded up

wheel hub

tyre
folded down

Figure 34: Potato Growing in Tyres

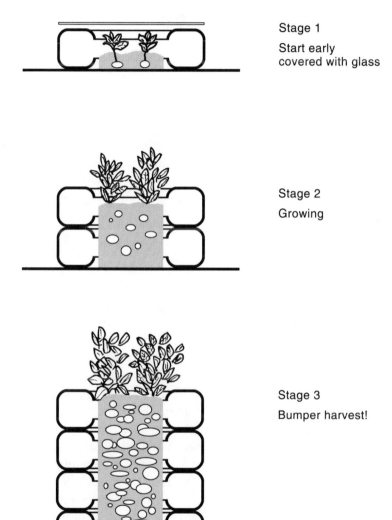

Stage 1
Start early
covered with glass

Stage 2
Growing

Stage 3
Bumper harvest!

85

24

LAWNS & MEADOWS

Lawns are heavy consumers. They use energy in their maintenance, manufacture and use of motorised mowers, strimmers, sweepers and perforators. They take up an excess of working hours in their care and management. They require regular watering, using enormous quantities of precious water. They are dosed with fertilisers, persistent weedkillers, moss killers and pesticides. This creates a poisonous sward on which we and our children relax and play. The soil is poisoned and so too, therefore, are the beneficial insects and animals (among them are the worms which, under normal circumstances, improve the soil and aerate it). The mowings are also unsuitable for composting or mulching.

If a lawn is required, try to keep it to a small area that you can mow in a short time with a hand mower (on a high setting). If you do not fertilise or water the lawn so much it will not grow as quickly and will not require cutting so often. Do not put any chemicals on your lawn. The mowings can then be used for mulching and composting and some herbs such as daisies and shepherd's purse can be eaten. The rest of the area can be used to grow useful plants, such as salad stuff, maybe with an emphasis on wild plants.

Another possibility is a spring wildflower meadow. Left uncut for the earlier months of the year, this offers a beautiful and diverse habitat of flowers and grasses for benefit of many insects and animals. It is then cut shorter during the summer months in much the same way as you would for a normal lawn. This gives you the opportunity to create a rich wildlife habitat for a small part of the year and an area on which you can relax and play in the warmest months of the year.

I once had a small meadow which was on the roof of a shed which was placed just outside the kitchen window. I nailed 3" timber around the edge, lined it with plastic and then two layers of carpet. Next I placed thick meadow turfs on top, scattered further wildflower seeds and planted bulbs. Then I just left it. It is still flowering 12 years later and is still a joy to see at eye level.

25

HEDGES

Hedges perform many functions such as defining boundaries, providing privacy, windbreaks, shelter, screens, shade, decoration or food. Hedges do not have to be a chore with regular cutting but can be used as another productive area. With selection of the right plants, they can provide a variety of fruits and other edibles. They can even consist of trained fruit trees. Hedges can be used as a support for climbing plants such as beans, nasturtiums, blackberries or winter squashes. They can also be underplanted with berries, such as raspberry, blackcurrant or gooseberry, and some of the more shade tolerant salads. The selection obviously depends on the space available.

Some Varieties for Hedges

Bamboo, *Pseudosass japonica.*
> Provides stakes and the young shoots are edible when cooked.

Beach plum, *Prunus maritima.*
> Small purple fruits. Eat cooked or in jam.

Cherry plum, *Prunus cerasifera.*
> Small yellow or red plums, good raw or in pies and jams.

Elderberry, *Sambucus nigra.*
> Flowers used for making fritters, cordial, wine and champagne. Fruit for wine, chutney, juice. It is worth trying the varieties that the Americans have done a breeding programme on; *Sambucas canadensis* is available from Clive Simms.

Golden currant, *Ribes aureum.*
>Small yellow or red fruit for jams and jellies.

Hazel, *Corylus avellana.*
>Yield nuts and coppiced poles.

Romanas rose, *Rosa ragosa.*
>Large edible fruits used for making jams, jellies or syrup. A favourite of geese as well.

Jerusalem artichoke, *Helianthus tuberosus.*
>Delicious root raw, baked or boiled.

Osier, *Salix viminalis.*
>Provide switches for basketry.

Sloe, *Prunus spinosa.*
>Berries used for making sloe gin, sloe and apple cheese or brined as olives.

These can be interspersed with a few hedgerow trees if space permits, such as:-

Bird cherry, *Prunus padus.*
>Winter fruit for birds or jam.

Crab apple, *Malus sylvestris.*
>Used for making cider and jelly.

Japanese raisin tree, *Hovenia dulcis.*
>Produces raisin like fruits.

Rowan, *Sorbus aucuparia.*
>For making rowan and apple jelly.

Wild service tree, *Sorbus torminalis.*
>Provides edible fruit when rotted.

And of course any of the top fruit trees.

26

FOREST GARDENS

The forest garden is another approach to gardening. Forest gardening is one of the oldest, as well as the most intensive and productive systems of producing food and other necessities ever devised. This abundant form of food production is used widely in tropical regions and has been adapted and pioneered in our temperate climate by Robert Hart in Shropshire. He observed that the forest, particularly at the edge, is extremely productive, far more so than a standard monoculture system.

The forest garden is modelled on the natural ecosystem of the forest and has a number of advantages. It is self maintaining as the leaves fall directly as a mulch where they are needed. There is tremendous diversity so that any pest or failures have a minimum effect. Plants that have a beneficial relationship can grow together (e.g. legumes put nitrogen into the soil to benefit other plants and many herbs deter insect pests and attract bees to pollinate fruit). A forest garden creates a mild and more humid microclimate and it needs little or no watering. Although it takes time to establish, maintenance is low consisting of mulching with straw, compost and weeds or comfrey which are cut on site, trimming back growth and cropping. Plants are laid out with undulating borders to increase the areas of edge, light and clearings.

A forest garden is designed on a seven storey stacking system (with examples of suitable plants):

1) Canopy of standard or half standard fruit trees:
   Apples, crab apples, damsons, gages, medlar, mulberry, pears, plums, quince.

2) Lower layer of dwarf fruit trees and hazels:
   Azerole, bamboo, cherry plum, cob, elderberry, filbert, rowan, wild service.

3) Shrub layer of soft fruit and other shrubs:
   Black, red and white currants, gooseberries, raspberries.

4) Herbaceous layer of herbs and perennial vegetables:
   Asparagus, borage, broom (to add nitrogen), cardoon, comfrey (for fertiliser), fennel, globe artichoke, lemon balm, lovage, marjoram, mints, nettles, rhubarb, rosemary, sage, tansy, tree onions.

5) Ground cover layer of low plants:
   Alpine strawberries, chard, chicory, claytonia, good king henry, land cress, purslane, ramsons, rocket, sorrel.

6) Rhizosphere of shade loving and winter roots:
   Hamburg parsley, horseradish, Jerusalem artichoke, salsify, scorzonera, winter radishes.

7) Vertical layer of climbing plants:
   Beans, blackberries, grape vines, nasturtium.

The forest garden can also be added to with fungi (which could include shitake, oyster mushroom or ceps) and anything else you can think of. Indigenous wild plants are ideal.

Figure 35: Different Layers of a Forest Garden

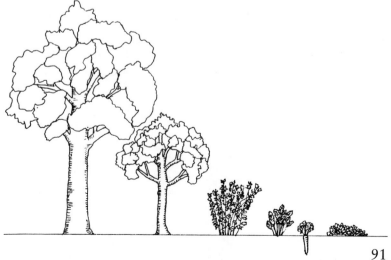

27

EDIBLE
ORNAMENTAL GARDENS

The simplest approach to achieving an edible garden is to replace all the elements in a garden with edible and useful plants. There is a vast selection of trees, shrubs, bushes, perennials, annuals and fungi with edible uses. The advantage of this approach is the potential diversity of produce, and new plants can always be added. (I have never known a gardener who could not find a space for something else.) This offers tremendous potential productivity and is still attractive as there are many ornamental yet edible plants. As ornamental plants are usually placed where they can be most readily seen, regular maintenance will be easier and more likely to be undertaken and this in turn will lead to increased productivity. By following the normal garden practice of having seed trays continually coming on as spaces become available, the garden can be filled to ensure cropping throughout the season.

Some annuals can be left to go to seed to supply swathes of seedlings to be either allowed to grow on or transplanted. These would include endives, lettuces, parsley, pot marigolds and salsify. A number of native wild plants are suitable and the whole range of fruits, salads and vegetables. Of course, the whole range of top and soft fruit can also be incorporated.

The following is a small selection of edible decorative trees, climbers and shrubs:

Trees

Azerole, *Crataegus azerolus.*
    Small tree edible fruit.

Butternut, *Juglans cinerea.*

Chinese persimmon, *Diospyros kaki.*
    Large shrub/small tree. Edible fruit in good summer.

Date plum, *Diospyros lotus.*
    Small tree with edible fruit.

Fig, *Ficus carica.*
    Edible fruit.

Heartnut, *Juglans ailantifolia.*

Honeyberry, *Celtis australis.*

Japanese raisin tree, *Hovenia dulcis.*
    Small tree with sweet swollen stems.

Kentucky coffee tree, *Gymnocladus dioica.*
    Seeds as coffee substitute. Legume.

Loquat, *Eriobotrya japonica.*
    Small tree with edible fruit.

Pear thorn, *Crataegus tomentosa.*
    Edible fruit.

Strawberry tree, *Arbutus unedo.*
    Small tree with edible fruit.

Sugar maple, *Acer saccharum.*
    Tap for sugar syrup.

Tree tomato, *Cyphomandra betacea.*
    Small tree with tomato like fruit.

Umbrella or stone pine, *Pinus pinea.*
    Large edible seeds.

Celtis sinesis.
    Small tree with edible fruit.

Shrubs

Autumn olive, *Elaeagnus umbellata.*
    Jams and jellies from fruit.

Blackcap, *Rubus leucodermis.*
    Edible berries.

Black haw, *Vibernum prunifolium.*
    Edible fruit.

Box blueberry, *Vaccinium ovatum.*
    Berries eaten raw or cooked.

Brazilian cherry, *Eugenia uniflora.*
    Edible fruit.

Carpobrotus deliciosus.
    Fig like fruit.

Cherry prinsepia, *Prinsepia sinensis.*
    Edible fruit.

Chilean guava, *Myrtus ugni.*
    Tender, edible fruit.

Christmas berry, *Heteromeles arbutifolia.*
    Edible berries.

Cornelian cherry, *Cornus mas.*
    Fruit for jams.

Cornus kousa chinensis.
    Strawberry-like fruit.

Fuchsia corymbiflora.
    Edible berries.

Guelder rose, *Viburnum opulus.*
    Native, fruit edible when cooked.

Japanese quince, *Chanenomeles.*
    Fruit for jam.

June berry/saskatoon, *Amelchier alnifolia.*
    Edible berries.

Mormon tea, *Ephedra nevadensis.*
    Tea from stems.

Oregon grape, *Mahonia repens.*
    Fruit for jams.

Pawpaw, *Asimina triloba.*
    Fruits in good summer.

Pigeon pea, *Cajanus cajun.*
    Peas and pods best eaten young. Legume.

Salal, *Gaultheria shallon.*
    Edible berries.

Salmonberry, *Rubus spectiblis.*

Siberian pea shrub, *Caragana arborescens.*
    Legume peas for chicken feed.

Thimble berry, *Rubus parviflorus.*
    Edible berries.

Thin leaved blueberry, *Vaccinium membranaceum.*

Water holly, *Mahonia nervosa.*
    Berries said to be edible.

Yellow cherry guava, *Psidium littorate lucidum.*
    Sensitive, edible fruit.

Climbers

American grape, *Vitis labrusca* hybrids.

American groundnut, *Apios americana.*
    Edible tubers.

Arctic beauty kiwi, *Actinidia kolomikta.*
    Less vigorous variety.

Apricot vine, *Passiflora incarnata.*
    Edible fruit.

Chocolate vine, *Akebia quinata.*
    Edible fruit.

Edible honeysuckle, *Lonicera edulis caerulea*.
Edible berries.

Kiwi fruit, *Actinidia deliciosa*.

Siberian kiwi, *Actinidia arguta*.

For more inspiration, visit places like RHS Wisley and Kew and other garden centres.

Figures 36/37/38:
Edible Ornamental Garden Layout Examples
(see pages 97-99)

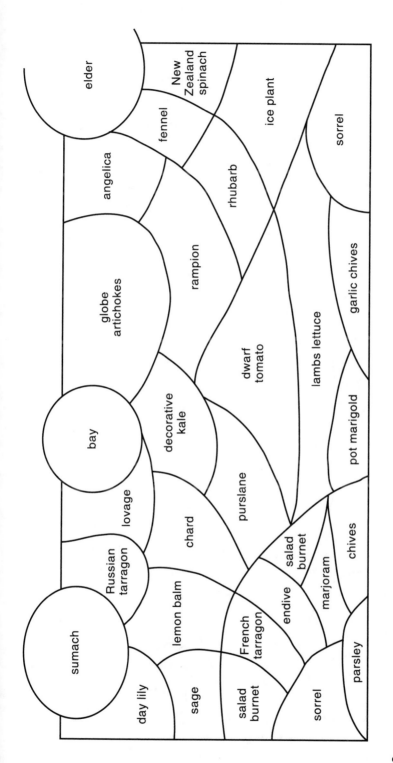

Figure 36: Edible Ornamental Layout Garden Example 1

97

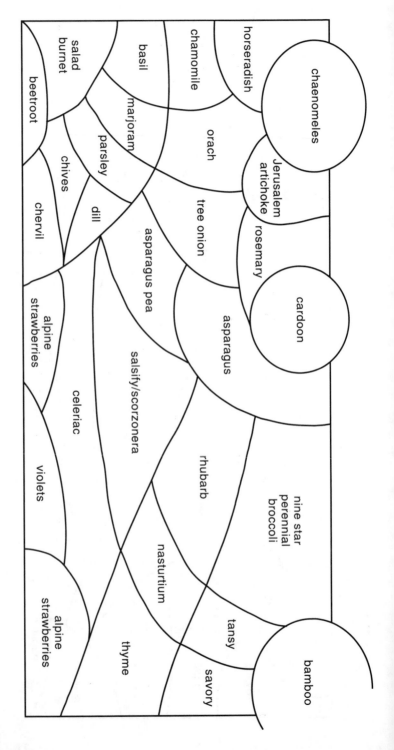

Figure 37: Edible Ornamental Garden Layout Example 2

98

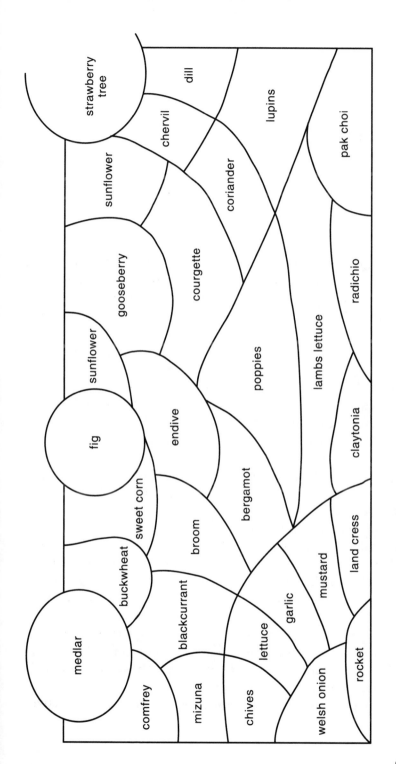

Figure 38: Edible Ornamental Garden Layout Example 3

99

28

PONDS

A pond is important for wildlife but it can also be used as an end point for a biological cleaning system for grey water, a catchment area for rainwater, a food production area, a reflector to direct more light into a house, a beautiful place to enjoy or all or some of these.

The junction between two ecologies, the ecotone, is generally the most productive of any area. It not only supports the plants of both ecologies but also some that are unique to itself. The junction between land and water is one of the most productive edges of all. To increase this edge area, make it crenellated (wavy). There should also be a deep area for fish. A small pond in the greenhouse will maintain the humidity in the hotter months and provide a habitat for beneficial insects and slug eaters to control greenhouse pests. The moment that your pond is made, it will start to be colonised by wildlife.

A small pond can be lined or cemented. When lining a pond, after removing any stones or other objects, first use sand followed by a pond liner. Then cover the pond liner with carpet as the top layer. This will help hold plants in place and provide a good base for them in which to become established. The carpet will also help protect the liner from being penetrated by the plants (or feet) and reduce the deterioration caused by the ultra violet rays of the sun.

If you decide to keep fish, consider using native fish such as carp or perch for eating. You could consider breeding koi carp as a money spinner.

Pond plants have prolific growth as well as being productive.

Many have a range of uses:

Arrow head, *Sagittaria sagittifolia*.
    Edible tubers when cooked.

Bogbean, *Menydinthus trifoliata*.
    Edible roots.

Bulrush, *Scirpus lacustris*.
    Roots can be eaten raw or dried and ground as flour.
    Edible young shoots. Leaves for basket weaving.

Bur-reed, *Sparganium erectum*.
    Edible tubers.

Cape pondweed, *Aponogeton distachyes*.
    Edible tubers and flowering spikes.

Common reed, *Phragmitis communis*.
    Dry and grind roots for porridge. Roast inner stems like
    marshmallow. Used to make thatch and baskets.

Flowering rush, *Butomus umbellatus*.
    Edible seeds as are the tubers when cooked.

Galingale, *Cyperus longus*.
    Edible roots. Can be used as a spice.

Golden saxifrage, *Chrysosplenium alternfolium*.
    Edible leaves.

Marsh marigold, *Caltha patustris*.
    Leaves and flower buds only edible if cooked.

Marsh woundwort, *Stachys palustris*.
    Young shoots can be eaten when boiled.

Pontederia cordata.
    Edible young leaves and seeds.

Small reed-mace, *Typha angustifolia latifolia*.
    Young leaves, young flower spikes and base of mature stems
    are edible. Rhizomes can be eaten raw, cooked or dried as
    flour. Leaves for basket weaving. Dried flowers give a mass
    of light material that can be used for insulation.

Sweet flag, *Acorus calamus.*
> Edible leaves. Dry rhizomes and lower stems to scent clothes and repel insects.

Water chestnut, *Trapa natans.*
> Not hardy. Seeds can be eaten raw or cooked.

Water cress, *Rorippa nasturtium aquaticum.*

Yellow water lily, *Nuphar lutea.*
> Roots and leaf stalks are edible.

Zizania latifolia.
> Young shoots, stem base and rhizomes are edible.

Figure 39: Plan and Section of Pond with Increased Edge

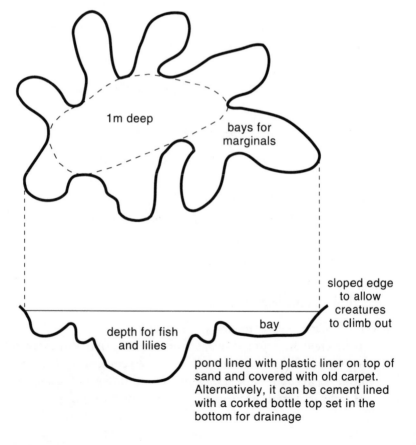

1m deep

bays for marginals

sloped edge to allow creatures to climb out

depth for fish and lilies

bay

pond lined with plastic liner on top of sand and covered with old carpet. Alternatively, it can be cement lined with a corked bottle top set in the bottom for drainage

29

SALADS

Salad plants are usually thought of as being eaten raw and there are a tremendous variety that will give you fresh food throughout the year. For this reason, they are probably the best choice of plants to grow where space is limited. On a plot the size of a double bed it is possible to have a good selection of green leaves, roots, flowers and fruit, cultivated and wild. A number of these suitable plants have strong flavours but add to the flavours and textures when a variety is mixed. Some are annuals, a number of which will self-seed if allowed to. Others are perennials, the roots of which you can leave in the ground to continue to grow time and time again. This works with a large variety of plants such as Florence fennel, radichio and some lettuces. You only want a few leaves of each at any one time for a mixed selection, so you should plan your planting to allow you to pluck or cut just what you need from day to day.

Winter

Most of the following plants will survive the winter, or at least recover and grow on if frosts are not too prolonged or if they are cloched: cabbage, chick weed, Chinese mustard, claytonia, endive, kale, lambs lettuce, land cress, mizuma, rocket, radichio, salad burnet and sorrel. Stored vegetables and some that will keep in the ground include: beetroot, carrots, celeriac, garlic, Hamburg parsley, Jerusalem artichoke, onion, parsnip, turnip and winter radishes, most of which can be eaten raw if sliced or grated. For forcing, there is chicory, radichio, salsify and seakale.

Spring

A few things are available early spring. Young hawthorn and lime leaves are good, as is hedge garlic. An early sowing of oriental turnip in a greenhouse, indoors or under a cloche is delicious. If the weather is right, there will be Florence fennel from last year's growth and also shoots from the scorzonera and salsify.

Summer

In early summer, you will have a combination of the last of the winter salads and the first of the summer. Leaf varieties include: alfalfa, celery, celtuce, chard, endive, fat hen, garland chrysanthemum, garlic chives, good king henry, land cress, lettuce, mustard, nasturtium, New Zealand spinach, orach, pot marigold, radichio, rocket, salad burnet, sorrel, spinach and summer purslane. Fruit and vegetable varieties include; courgette, cucumber, mangetout, peppers, tomato, radish seed pods, and young french beans. Flower varieties include: borage, day lily, edible chrysanthemum, nasturtium, *pelargoniums,* pot marigold, primrose, rose, violet, and most herb flowers. Some varieties of herbs will add flavour to a salad, such as chives, fennel, mint and tarragon.

Figure 40: Small Salad Bed - Winter

Perennial	salad burnet	garlic chives		French sorrel
	Florence fennel	good king henry		chives
Annual	claytonia	land cress	rocket	mustard
	radichio	mizuna	endive	winter radish
	kale	carrot	cabbage	lambs lettuce

Figure 41: Small Salad Bed - Summer

salad burnet	garlic chives		French sorrel
Florence fennel	good king henry		chives
NZ spinach	orach	purslane	endive
lettuce	celtuce	rocket	mustard
land cress	radish	marigold	chrysanthemum
radichio	celery	ice plant	nasturtium
garlic	sugar peas	carrot	bunching onions
kohl rabi	turnip	beet	chard

Perennial (rows 1–2)

Annual (rows 3–8)

30

WILD FOOD

Wild food is available for those who want to make a little effort. There is so much that is available. Although some species are not wild, they can often be for free. Ensure that you can properly identify them and check the legality of picking. There are some good books available that will help you find what is edible. (If you look at a hedgerow during a hot summer you will see that wild plants are well adapted to our climate and will flourish even when our gardens look the worse for wear. Indigenous plants should play a large part in our gardens for this reason.)

The following are a few suggestions of wild food and other food that can be found for free:

Feed

Collect trimmings and spoilt vegetables from the greengrocers or market. Some may even be edible for yourselves. The rest can go to the animals or be composted.

Bread

Ask a baker if he will let you have his stale bread for animal feed. What he gives you may not always be stale and can go to make good bread pudding.

Fish

Many coarse fish such as pike, carp or perch make good eating, as do eels. But they can taste awful if the water is polluted. Ask a local fisherman for his catch. Go on a sea fishing trip when the mackerel are running. On a good day it is possible to stock up for the year. They can be salted, smoked, frozen or pickled. I could no longer eat fish from a fishmongers once I had tasted the fresh ones I had caught. For those by the sea, another bonus is the numerous shellfish that are available.

Fruit

Throughout the autumn and late summer, there are many wild fruits such as blackberry, bilberry, crab apples, elderberry, gueldar rose, rose-hips, rowan, sloes and wild service. Spring is a good time to find them, when the plants are in blossom (the white flowers of sloe are the first to appear). It is then possible to go straight to them when you want to harvest.

You can find many an orchard where the owners are only too pleased to let you pick their surplus produce.

Look out for sweet chestnut, hazel and walnut.

Fungi

There is a large range of edible fungi. Ensure that they can be identified (most have particular hosts or habitats). All can be dried for storage.

Meat

Many landowners are plagued with rabbits and are happy to let you catch them on their land. It is possible to shoot them with an air rifle, use a ferret or live trap them. Pigeons are another tasty pest which can be trapped or shot.

Vegetables

Throughout the year there are many vegetables, salads and fungi available. Many allotment holders produce a surplus and are willing to exchange.

Seaweed

There are a large number of edible seaweeds that can be collected fresh and dried for storage. Seaweed also makes a wonderful fertiliser. It is most readily available in quantity on the seashore after a storm. Be aware of polluted beaches.

Snails

Many gardeners will thank you for collecting this delicacy. The brown common garden snail, *Helix aspersa,* is a pest in most gardens. They are low in calories, high in protein and rich in minerals. Do not collect where poisons have been used.

Collecting

Snails are best collected a few hours after dark as they are nocturnal. Collect the larger ones as they are tastier, there is more to eat and the shells are stronger. If the weather is dry they will seal themselves in, so water the collection area in the late afternoon before harvesting.

Purging

They must be purged to get rid of the flavour from what they have been eating. Put them in a container with about 12mm of moist corn or oatmeal in the bottom. Put a ventilated top on it, such as muslin or a wire mesh, and store in a cool, shady area for 72 hours. Discard any that are inactive on the bottom. Take them out and rinse them in cool water and blanch them. If you want to keep them longer, change their meal every two days to stop them going sour.

Blanching

Plunge the snails into boiling water and simmer for 15 minutes. Then drain. Remove them from their shells with a toothpick, remove the dark coloured gall, a dark spiral on the tail end, then wash them several times in cold water. They may then be cooked or frozen. If you want to use the shells for serving, boil them for 30 minutes in water that has a quarter of a teaspoon of baking soda to every pint. Wash under cold water and dry.

Cooking

They can be boiled, baked or fried for about 10 minutes. The classic dish is with garlic butter. For three people, take 18 snails and simmer for 10 minutes in a cup of stock made with wine, bay leaf, spices and onion. Save the liquid. Place some garlic butter in the shells, put in the snail and top with garlic butter, breadcrumbs and cheese, as desired. Place in a shallow pan with a little of the liquid and bake at 450°F for about 8 minutes.

Bon appétit!

Animals

31

ANIMALS - GENERAL

Animals perform a number of functions. They can be kept as pets, for their therapeutic value, security, companionship, pest control or as suppliers of useful products. Whatever their function, animals are usually totally dependent on you, so you must be prepared to take responsibility for their well-being. The ongoing health of your animals is of obvious importance. Careful observation, knowledge of your particular varieties and familiarity with them will enable you instantly to see if they fall ill.

Before Buying

Before buying, research into the conditions that your choice of stock will require. Find out how much maintenance they will require and if they have any special needs. Check on their normal feed requirements, as any sudden change of diet can upset an animal. Make sure that there are no local restrictions on keeping livestock. Have the housing, equipment and feed ready before purchase. Housing is usually quite easy to make. Shuttering ply is a good material as it will stand up to weathering and can often be obtained from building sites. Hay and straw are very cheap when bought direct from a farm. The price of a bale is often about the same as for a bag from the pet shop. If a bale is too much, share it with a friend. The same applies to feed, buy it from an agricultural feed supplier and share it if necessary.

Buying

Study a large variety of animals at shows, exhibitions and auctions. However, do not be seduced by show varieties. They might look pretty, but they are usually bred for their cosmetic appearance and to conform to showing standards rather than for their productivity or hardiness. Buy the best quality commercial breeds where possible. Do not economise when buying stock. It is better to economise on housing.

Visit breeders and ask a lot of questions. If possible, buy from them rather than an intermediate dealer. A breeder will give you more information and back up advice and you will therefore be better able to assess the condition of the stock. Animals bought direct from them will also suffer less trauma as they will 'change hands' less frequently.

32

SUITABLE ANIMALS

Animals add an extra dimension to your environment. I cannot imagine not having animals around. They can also provide a number of useful products. The following is a selection of the animals that could be of use in an urban environment:

Bantams

Bantams are small chickens and will therefore give you small eggs.

Bees

Bees can be kept in a small garden or on a roof to give wonderful honey, wax, propolis and to ensure the pollination of fruit.

Budgerigars

The word comes from the Aborigine words for 'parrot' and 'good to eat'!

Cats

Storage of feedstuff for various livestock can attract rats and mice. Cats can control these. They need meat to survive and can largely do so on such a wild diet. This can be supplemented with fishmonger's and butcher's scraps (including offal).

Chickens

Chickens will supply fresh eggs and, if you have a cockerel, replacement stock and meat. Do not let them roam in the garden as they are likely to do a lot of damage. Chickens let onto a vegetable patch at the end of a season will clear the ground of pests and pest eggs and will fertilise the ground at the same time.

Dogs

If you have a dog, feed it on butcher's scraps and leftovers. Dogs can adapt to a vegetarian diet. The Vegetarian Society provides recommendations.

Ducks

Ducks lay more eggs than chickens and do not do much damage roaming the garden. Ducks are particularly partial to slugs.

Geese

A couple of goslings at the beginning of the season will keep the grass down. They also give a fine Christmas dinner.

Guinea Pigs

These are kept to give meal size helpings of meat and are regarded as a delicacy in South America!

Pigeons

Pigeons give a regular supply of meat, some eggs and high quality manure. They collect most of their own feed.

Quail

These quiet little birds will give a regular supply of delicate eggs and, if you wish, delicious meat.

Rabbits

Three rabbits, a buck and two does will keep you in a steady supply of meat, skins and manure.

33

BEES

Bees will give you delicious honey which will put you off commercially produced honey forever. They will also give you wax, propolis and ensure that you have full pollination of your crops.

They can be kept on flat roofs and balconies as well as in the garden. Consider carefully, however, where you are going to position them as they cannot be moved easily; unless the bees are moved very gradually (only 3 feet at a time) or to a site at least 3 miles away, they will return to the old site and perish. They will need some sort of screen to send their flight path up if space is limited. Once you have them, you will only need to look at them briefly each week during the summer.

Bees generally do very well in urban situations as they have plenty of forage from all the flowers in gardens and parks. If the weather is reasonable, you could expect anything up to 100lb of honey a year from a hive. It is important to have some water available near the hive.

In an urban situation, it is important to have gentle bees, so stock with a queen from a known line such as a New Zealand queen. The best way to learn beekeeping is to join your local beekeeping club. Be warned! It is a fascinating hobby and can be quite expensive to set up. But with a few good years, a hive will have paid for itself.

Forage

As the majority of bee forage is outside your site, it might be an idea to consider some suitable forage plants for your garden, such as *anchusia, arabis, aubretia, berberis,* blackberry, borage, buckthorn, *buddleia, campanula,* canterbury bell, *centaurea, clarkia,* cornflower, cotoneaster, cranesbill, crocus, dahlia, *erica,* forget-me-not, fuchsia, *genista, gilia,* heliotrope, hollyhock, honeysuckle, hyacinth, *limnanthes, linaria,* mallow, michaelmas daisy, mignonette, narcissus, *phacelia,* poppy, *ribes,* rosebay willowherb, *salvia,* scabious, *sedum, sidalcea,* snowdrop, thistle, *verbascum, veronica,* violet and wallflower. Lime trees produce a beautiful honey. A willow is useful for early pollen and, standing below the tree, the buzz of busy bees in early spring is delightful.

34

CHICKENS

Chickens will give you a regular supply of delicious fresh eggs to eat or to barter. They are a pleasure to listen to, can be watched for hours and are very easy to keep.

Varieties

There are a number of commercial varieties that have been bred with light body weight for maximum conversion of food to eggs. These are hybrids so will not breed true. This is not generally a consideration as regulations do not allow you to keep a cockerel in most urban environments in any case. This is unfortunate as it destroys the natural pattern of chicken behaviour. If you wish to keep some of the old dual purpose breeds which were intended for eating and egg laying, you can buy Cuckoo Marans, Welsummer or Rhode Island Reds, all of which are very attractive birds. One of the classic crosses is the Rhode Island X Light Sussex. Try to buy commercial varieties rather than show birds as the egg laying will be better.

Housing

Chickens will happily roost in trees, but this makes them difficult to catch and vulnerable to foxes. A house can be as rough as you like, so spend your money on good stock rather than a stately chicken house. The house needs to be waterproof, foxproof, well ventilated and with easy access for cleaning out. Perches should be about 2" wide with rounded edges. These should be tiered so the 'top' chicken can have the higher perch, thus maintaining the hierarchy. Nest boxes should be about a 12" cube, open at the

118

front with a 2" lip on the front edge and some strips of cloth hanging in front to give some privacy. One nest box to about 5 chickens should be enough. It should have straw in it and not hay. Nest boxes can be positioned to allow you access from the outside or can be positioned within the house itself.

Ark

A run attached to a small house on wheels can be moved around on the lawn. If made the width of the vegetable beds, it can be placed so the chickens can clean them of weeds, grubs and insects whilst manuring at the same time.

Figure 42: Chicken Ark

Forage

Chickens are a jungle fowl and so prefer a heavily planted run. It can contain a large variety of plants which can also supply some of their feed. These include beans, brassicas, broom, buckwheat, *buddleia,* cherry plums, comfrey, cotoneaster, crab apples, currants (any kind), damsons, dandelion, elder, fat hen, grains, grass, Jerusalem artichoke, marigold, mulberry, rowan, salads (all kinds), salsify, sedge, shepherd's purse, Siberian pea tree, squashes, sunflowers and virtually anything that humans would eat.

Runs

If the run is positioned next to the vegetable patch, trimmings can be thrown directly to the chickens. Separate runs with access from a straw yard surrounding the house will allow them to be used in rotation. Runs should have netting up to about 1.5 metres high without a rail at the top. If the chickens start flying over the top, clip one wing just past the end bone.

Figure 43: Possible Chicken Run Arrangement

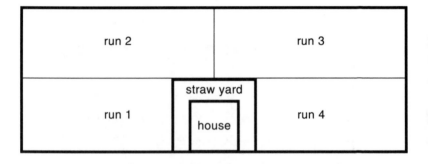

Figure 44: Wing Clipping

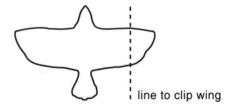

Feeding

Chickens need about 4oz of pellets or mash a day per chicken, plus household scraps. You can substitute about half the pellets with grain. To digest the food they need grit which can be bought, but coarse sand will do. Some sort of calcium is also needed, such as oyster shells or ground up baked eggshells. Extra protein can be supplied by placing some flesh scraps, or what the cat has caught, in a small mesh container suspended over the run to keep it out of the reach of mice and rats and to stop the chickens eating. Chickens love chasing and eating the flies and the maggots that drop from the container. If you have a worm bin, they will love eating the worms too.

Water

They must have water at all times. Keep a couple of cloves of garlic in it as this helps to stop parasitic worms and keep them healthy. Water can be supplied automatically from a water butt filled from the roof of the house using a stop cock to regulate it. A pipe inserted into the butt just below the top will allow the gnat larvae to overflow into the drinking water giving the chickens more protein.

Eggs

Eggs should be stored pointed end down. If they are dirty, clean them with warm water. If you wish to sell eggs, your hens must be regularly tested for salmonella. To maintain egg laying through the winter, you will need to supplement the light in the morning to give 14 hours a day. Introduce any new stock at night.

General

A dust bath is essential to keep them mite free. A herbal insecticide can be put in it.

Clean the house out twice yearly, either use a blow lamp after brushing or a lime wash. Creosote can burn the chickens.

A large hen house can be used to produce enriched compost. Simply throw in lawn mowings, leaves, vegetable trimmings, weedings and household scraps as well as throwing in a few handfuls of grain morning and evening. The chickens will turn it whilst enriching it, then all you have to do is dig it out when it is ready.

35

COMBINED
CHICKEN HOUSE/GREENHOUSE

One of the permaculture 'orthodoxies' is the combined henhouse and greenhouse. This demonstrates how elements can be combined to benefit each other. Water for the greenhouse and chickens is collected from the roof. Carbon dioxide from the chickens is used by the plants and the oxygen from the plants used by the chickens. In winter, the greenhouse keeps the chickens warm so they use less food and the chickens contribute towards this warmth with their body heat. Any surplus food or trimmings from the greenhouse can be thrown to the chickens and any organic matter put into the henhouse will produce an enriched compost for the greenhouse.

Figure 45:
Combined Chicken House/Greenhouse
(see page 123)

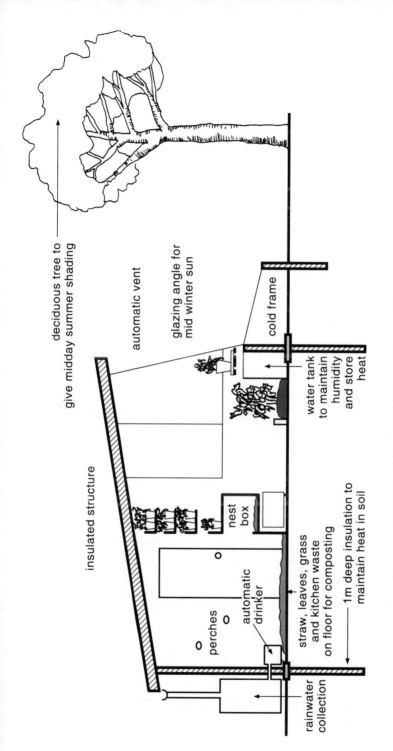

deciduous tree to
give midday summer shading

automatic vent

glazing angle for
mid winter sun

insulated structure

nest box

perches

automatic drinker

cold frame

water tank
to maintain
humidity and store
heat

straw, leaves, grass
and kitchen waste
on floor for composting

1m deep insulation to
maintain heat in soil

rainwater
collection

Figure 45: Combined Chicken House/Greenhouse

123

36

DUCKS

Ducks are lovely to have in the garden. They rush around in groups quacking quietly to each other. They do very little damage and keep the garden clear of slugs and snails. They love water to splash in to keep clean. The only real damage they can do is to an ornamental pond.

Varieties

The best ducks for egg laying are Khaki Campbells or Indian Runners. These both produce more eggs than a hen. A more decorative bird is the Welsh Harlequin, which is a 'chance mutation' from the Khaki Campbell.

Housing

Housing need only be very simple and big enough for the ducks to sit and lay. A box with a wide door is important as they all tend to rush out at once in the morning. When you first get them, shut them in for three days with plenty of water and feed them in the house. Then they will see their box as home and return there to be fed in the evenings. Put a good layer of sawdust, woodshavings or straw on the floor. They are messy, so you will need to clear out the house at regular intervals. This waste is very good for your compost.

Feed

About 6oz of chicken pellets a day per duck and plenty of water in a deep container.

Eggs

They tend to drop their eggs anywhere and usually in the morning, so let them out at mid morning and collect the eggs then. Clean them straightaway with warm water if necessary as duck eggs are porous. A straw nest in one corner with a china egg in it can help encourage laying.

37

PIGEONS

All pigeons are good to eat. They have been domesticated for centuries for their squabs (young pigeons) and phosphate rich manure. One advantage is that they are self foraging.

Housing

You can have a fancy loft but any sort of weatherproof container will do with access holes about 6" x 6" and shelves 8" deep with lips on them. Of course, you need an access door from which to collect the eggs, squabs and manure. Lofts can take the form of a tower, be fixed on the side of the house or on a pole, as long as the cat cannot get in.

Feeding

A few handfuls of grain each day. This is fun to do and it supplements their food, especially in winter. Also, throw some in the house when the females are feeding the young.

Squabs

Squabs are young pigeons. They are lumpy and ugly, can be heavier than the parents and are ready for eating at about 4 weeks old. If you do not want constant young, take the eggs out and eat them.

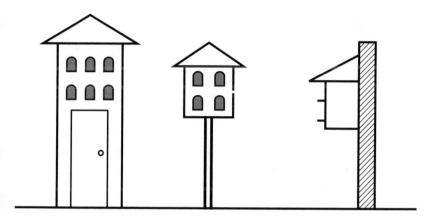

38

QUAIL

These lovely little birds are very discrete, giving the occasional cheep or trill and produce about 300 eggs a year.

A good laying variety is the Coturnix, known as European or Japanese quail. You can keep up to 6 females with one male.

Housing

The biggest problem is rats, so any housing needs fine mesh all round it. I keep mine in a small ark on wheels on the lawn in the summer. This has an enclosed area to one end with a small pop hole for the quail and access doors at each end for me. In the winter, keep them undercover and supplement the lighting to give a total of 14 hours a day to maintain egg laying. When they are startled, they fly straight upwards, so line the roof with bubble foam to stop them hurting themselves.

Feed

Quail need a constant supply of water. They require a high protein diet such as pheasant or chick crumbs plus some greenery. Sprouted alfalfa is good in winter. Of course, any flies caught in a fly trap are welcome.

Eggs

Eggs can be eaten fresh having been hard boiled for 1 minute, or then pickled in a vinegar solution or brine. They can also be sold fresh.

39

RABBITS

Rabbits are quiet, easy to keep and will give a cheap supply of meat which is high in protein and low in cholesterol. They will also give furs and high quality manure which can go in the worm bin, on the compost or straight onto the garden. Handle them early in life and it will make caring for them much easier.

Breeds

All varieties of rabbits are good to eat. If keeping them specifically for meat, a New Zealand doe with a Californian buck is a good combination if you intend to feed them on concentrates. They will reach a slaughter weight in 8 - 10 weeks. If you are feeding them a more extensive diet of greenstuff, kitchen waste, vegetables and grass, some of the older breeds, such as the Flemish, British Giant or the Chinchilla Giganta are more suitable. They take longer to reach their final weight of about 12lb plus.

Housing

Housing should be dry, clean and draftproof, but rabbits do need plenty of fresh air and can tolerate extreme cold.

Rabbits should not be kept together as they will fight, but they are happier if they can see each other. To breed, they need at least 14 hours of light a day, so in the winter this needs to be supplemented. Indirect light is better than direct sunlight so they do not get too hot. Solid housing floors can get very wet, so they need plenty of bedding which should be changed frequently. The housing should be large enough, about 1.5 by 0.6 metres is a good size for one rabbit, with an enclosed area to one end. Wire mesh cage housing can be positioned over worm bins to convert the debris into fine worm compost.

Feeding

When you purchase a rabbit, find out what they have been fed on. A change to a new diet should be over about a two week period to allow the stomach flora to adapt. They must always have roughage in the form of hay or straw. It is far cheaper to buy a bale from a farm or stable. Rabbits must have fresh water available at all times, a drinker from a large bottle is suitable.

Feeding can be with pellets or greenstuff, or a combination.

Rabbits require approximately 3 - 4oz of pellets a day per rabbit. Those bought from a pet shop can contain very low protein levels and be very expensive, so it is better to purchase the commercial pellets used by breeders. If you have difficulty finding a supplier, approach the local rabbit club.

Greenstuff can be collected from the hedgerow, but make sure that you know which plants are poisonous. Another source is trimmings from the greengrocer or market, as well as your own and your neighbour's kitchen waste. Alternatively, grow your own alfalfa, beetroot, broad red clover, carrots, chicory, kale, and kohl rabi.

Breeding

Do not breed rabbits before 25 weeks old. Introduce the doe to the buck in his pen or a neutral place. Stand by to stop the doe from attacking the buck! Once pregnant, give the doe greenstuff even if she is not used to it and increase her feed to about double the normal. At about 26 days, she will start to make a nest and should give birth at about 32 days; if she has not delivered by 34 days, either something may be wrong or she is not pregnant. A few hours after the birth, move her to a familiar place, remove any dead ones and cull the small and the weak to leave the 7 most healthy. At three weeks, increase the amount of feed to allow for the young to wean.

Slaughter

This is very quick and easy. Get someone from the local rabbit club to show you how.

Epilogue

40

DO IT!

Why not have a sustainable future? Why not have a rich full life in a beautiful, safe, supportive environment? Why not have worthwhile jobs that leave time for a variety of activities? Why not have a rich social life with lots of fun? Why not make our cities into a collection of villages that are fit places to live in? Why not have our gardens, parks and public spaces laden with plants for food, medicine and fuel? Why not have corridors for wildlife penetrating our cities? Why not have recycling plants to reuse or recycle waste (including human excreta that could fertilise our soil after methane extraction)? Why not have local power generation linked with recycling and water? Surplus heat could then be used for water or space heating, growing under glass or swimming pools. Why not have community care for the sick, old, young, and the lonely in their own community? Why not share with the people around you? Why not...

In the end, it is all down to us. It is no good whingeing, 'What can I do?' It is totally clear what we can do. In the first place, we need to literally 'put our own houses in order'. From this point, we can then extend our influence into the community by example, by our lifestyles. Then we have a hope of changing our society and its values, and transforming it into a better place.

Appendix 1

SOURCES OF PLANTS & SEEDS

ACORN LANDSCAPES
Y-Fron, Llawr-y-Glyn, Caersws, Powys SY17 5RJ
(05516) 283
Trees and shrubs with a good selection of willows such as osier, violet, purple, golden and biomass willow.

CHASE ORGANICS
Coombelands House, Coombelands Lane, Addlestone, Weybridge, Surrey KT15 1HY
(0932) 858511
Have now combined with HDRA. Suppliers of organic seeds, green manures and organic fertilisers etc. Good selection of oriental vegetables and they supply the best hoe I know called the Swiss reciprocating hoe.

CHILTERN SEEDS
Bortree Stile, Ulverston, Cumbria LA12 7PB
(0229) 581137
A tremendous selection of tree, shrub, vegetable and herb seeds.

CLIVE SIMMS
Woodhurst, Essendine, Stamford, Lincolnshire PE9 4LQ
(0780) 55615
A good selection of edible plants, including an American selected elder.

FUTURE FOODS
3, Tai Madog, Stablau, Llanrug, Gwynedd LL55 3PH
(0286) 870606
A wonderful selection of unusual food plants, including edible fungi spawn.

DART TREES
17, Arden Drive, Chelston, Torquay, Devon TQ2 6DZ
A range of useful trees and shrubs.

DEACONS NURSERY
Godshill, Isle of Wight PO38 3HW
(0983) 840750
Good selection of fruit trees and bushes.

HILLIER NURSERIES
Ampfield House, Nr. Romsey, Hampshire SO51 9PA
(0794) 68787
Large selection of trees and shrubs.

PLANTS FOR A FUTURE
The Field, Higher Penpol, St. Veep, Lostwithiel,
Cornwall PL22 0NE
(0208) 873554
Tremendously knowledgeable about useful plants.

SCOTT'S NURSERIES
Merriott, Somerset TA16 5PL
(0460) 72306
Fruit, nuts, trees and shrubs.

SUFFOLK HERBS
Sawyers Farm, Little Cornard, Sudbury, Suffolk CO10 0NY
(0787) 227247

THOMPSON & MORGAN
London Road, Ipswich, Suffolk IP2 0BA
(0473) 688821
A variety of unusual plants.

One way of obtaining plants is to propagate cuttings. You can either obtain these from friends or buy a few plants and cut them up. Cuttings can be taken from most soft fruit and a large number of shrubs. Layering is also useful; this is done by pegging a branch into the ground until it roots. If you have established decorative cherry or crab apple trees, it is possible to graft fruiting varieties onto these.

Appendix 2

ORGANISATIONS

CENTRE FOR ALTERNATIVE TECHNOLOGY
The Quarry, Machynlleth, Powys SY20 9AZ
(0654) 702400
Interesting place to visit and they run good courses.

CHELSEA PHYSIC GARDEN
Royal Hospital Road, London SW3
071-352 5646
Old, established gardens.

CO-COUNSELLING PHOENIX
5 Victoria Road, Broomhill, Sheffield S10 2DJ
(0742) 686371
Co-counselling centre for information.

HENRY DOUBLEDAY RESEARCH ASSOCIATION
Ryton on Dunsmore, Coventry CU8 3LG
(0203) 303517
Organic growing demonstration gardens and heritage seed bank.

ECOLOGICAL DESIGN ASSOCIATION
20 High Street, Stroud, Gloucestershire GL5 1AS
(0453) 752985
Promotes ecological design.

ENERGY TECHNOLOGY SUPPORT UNIT
Building 156, AEA, Harwell, Didcot OX11 0RA
(0235) 432450
Renewable energy enquiries bureau. Free leaflets and reports.

FINDHORN FOUNDATION
Cluny College, Forres IV36 0RD
(0309) 672288
New Age community running spirituality orientated courses.

INSTITUTE OF SOCIAL INVENTIONS
24, Abercorn Place, London NW8 9XP
081-229 7253
Encourages new and imaginative non technical ideas. Offers
many useful publications.

INTERMEDIATE TECHNOLOGY DEVELOPMENT GROUP
Myson House, Railway Terrace, Rugby CV21 3HT
(0788) 60631
Deploys appropriate technology to the Third World.

KEW GARDENS
Kew, London TW9 3AH
081-940 1171
Established plants from around the world.

LETSLINK UK NETWORK
61 Woodcock Road, Warminster, Wiltshire BA12 9DH
(0985) 217871
National office and coordination centre for LETS groups. Also
gives out information on starting your own LETSystem.

LONDON ECOLOGY CENTRE
45, Shelton Street, Covent Garden, London WC2H 9HJ
081-379 4324
Centre for meetings, exhibitions and has a small shop.

NATIONAL FRUIT COLLECTION
The Brogdale Horticultural Trust, Brogdale Road, Faversham, Kent ME13 8XZ
(0795) 590272
Vast range of top and soft fruit. An opportunity to taste before you buy.

NATIONAL PURE WATER ASSOCIATION
Meridan, Caegoody Lane, Ellesmere, Shropshire SY12 9DW
(0691) 623015
Aims to improve the quality of the nation's water.

NETWORK FOR ALTERNATIVE TECHNOLOGY AND TECHNOLOGY ASSESSMENT
c/o Energy and Environment Research Unit,
The Open University, Walton Hall, Milton Keynes MK7 6AA
(0908) 74066
Produces newsletter and booklets on alternative technology issues.

PERMACULTURE ASSOCIATION (Britain)
PO Box 1, Buckfastleigh, Devon, TQ11 0LH
(03643) 333
Registered charity connecting people, ideas, resources and projects worldwide, as well as organising training courses.

REED BEDS
Camphill Water, Oaklands park, Newnham,
Gloucestershire GL14 1EF
(0594) 516063
1st Monday in the month at 3pm for guided tour.

ROBERT HART'S FOREST GARDEN
Highwood Hill, Rushbury, Church Stretton, Shropshire SY6 7DE
(06943) 342
Ring or write with SAE to arrange a visit.

ROYAL HORTICULTURAL SOCIETY GARDENS
Wisley, Woking, Surrey GU23 6QB
(0483) 224234
Extensive gardens open to the public.

SOIL ASSOCIATION
86 Colston Street, Bristol BS1 5BB
(0272) 290661
Promotes and supports organic growing.

TIR GAIA SOLAR VILLAGE
Llwyn Lane, Rhayader, Powys LD6 5DY
(0597) 810929
Development project that also runs courses.

WOMEN'S ENVIRONMENTAL NETWORK
Aberdeen Studios, 22 Highbury Grove, London N5 2EA
071-490 2511
Very active women's group.

WORKING WEEKENDS ON ORGANIC FARMS (WWOOF)
19, Bradford Road, Lewes, Sussex BN17 1RB
(0273) 476286
Arranges for people to work on organic farms in exchange for board, lodging, information and country life.

Appendix 3

BOOKS

Books and other publications available direct from:
Permanent Publications
Hyden House Limited, Little Hyden Lane, Clanfield,
Hampshire PO8 0RU. Tel: (0705) 596500

The Barefoot Homoeopath - Health Care for the Whole Person
Madeleine Harland & Glen Finn; Hyden House.
Comprehensive, simple to use and jargon-free guide to
do-it-yourself homoeopathy.

Permaculture Magazine - Solutions for Sustainable Living
Published quarterly by Permanent Publications in co-operation
with the Permaculture Association (Britain).
Fully illustrated with articles, designs, projects, news and solutions
from Britain and all over the world.

Permaculture in a Nutshell; Patrick Whitefield;
Permanent Publications.
Superbly clear and accessibly written introduction to permaculture.

The Permaculture Plot; Permanent Publications.
Lists over 50 places where you can see permaculture in operation.

A number of other books with special reference to permaculture
can be obtained from:
Eco-logic Books
20 Gastard Lane, Gastard, Corsham, Wiltshire SN13 9QN.

Other Recommended Reading

After the Crash; Guy Dauncey; Green Print.
Information on alternative economies.

Blueprint For a Green Planet; John Seymour; Dorling Kindersley.
Lots to think about and do.

Co-counselling Manual; Gretchen Pyves. 195, Holcombe Rd., Helmshore, Rossendale, Lancashire BB4 4NY.

The Complete Book of Massage; Clare Maxwell Hudson; Dorling Kindersley.
Tells you most of what you need to know.

The Complete Book of Raising Livestock and Poultry; Katie Thear; Martin Dunitz.
Very thorough.

Creating Abundance; Andrew Ferguson; Piatkus Books
New attitudes to living. A must for permaculturists.

Designing and Maintaining Your Edible Landscape Naturally; Robert Kourik; Metamorphic Press.
A very thorough book.

Food For Free; Richard Mabey; Fontana.
Good but needs another book to identify the plants.

The Food Scandal; Caroline Walker; Century.
Read all about it!

Forest Gardening; Robert A de J Hart; Green Books.
Full details of how the author arrived at and organised this fascinating idea.

The Fruit Finder; Lawrence D. Hills; HDRA.
Answers the vexing question of where to find the varieties you want.

Grow Your Own Chinese Vegetables; Geri Harrington; Gerden Ways Publishing.
A good range of little known vegetables.

The Hillier Manual of Trees and Shrubs; David and Charles.
Superb reference.

Home Ecology; Karen Christensen; Arlington Books.
Wonderful book on all aspects of the home with plentiful references.

The House Of The Future; Terence McLaughlin; Independent TV Books.
Slightly dated, but a clear survey.

Home Preservation of Fruit and Vegetables; HMSO.
The definitive book.

The Integral Urban House; Farallones Institute; Sierra Club Books.
A full write up of this Californian house, with lots of charts and diagrams.

The Integrated Garden; A. M. Clevely; Barrie Jenkins.
Plenty of ideas for decorative edible growing.

Introduction To Permaculture; Bill Mollison; Tagari.
His most recent book for all climates.

Linking Farmers to Consumers; Mandy Pullen; International Society for Ecology & Culture.
Available from The Soil Association.
Discusses standard ordering systems, subscription farming, community supported agriculture and combined ordering systems, giving working examples.

Mushrooms in the Garden; Helmut Steineck; Mad River Press, California.
Cultivation of a great variety.

The Natural House Book; David Pearson; Conran Octopus.
Makes you wonder how we can survive in our homes, let alone in
the outside environment.

Organic Gardening; Lawrence D. Hills; Penguin.
The classic book from the founder of the Henry Doubleday
Association.

Oriental Vegetables; Joy Larkcom; John Murray.
All you want to know.

A Pattern Language; Christopher Alexander; Oxford University.
Can't be beaten for looking at houses and their groupings in
relation to people.

Permaculture - A Designers' Manual; Bill Mollison; Island Press.
The complete detailed account of all aspects of permaculture.

The Permaculture Way; Graham Bell; Thorsons.
A very readable overview.

The Personal Management Handbook; John Mulligan; Sphere.
Good coverage on aspects of personal development.

The Plant Finder; edited by Tony Lord; The Hardy Plant Society.
Lists over 40,000 plant names and where to obtain them.

Planting Native Trees and Shrubs; K. and G. Beckett; Jarrold.
Excellent guide to growing condition and guilds.

Resource Manual For A Living Revolution; Virginia Coover;
New Society Publishers.
On the organisation and running problems of a community.
The Salad Garden; Joy Larkcom; Frances Lincoln.
The best book on growing all year round salads.

Seaweed - A Users Guide; Sonia Surey-Gent; Whittet Books.
How to identify, preserve and cook.

Shelter; Shelter Publications IC.
Available from Home Book Services, PO Box 650, Bolinas, California 94924, USA.
Fascinating book on unconventional building methods.

The Survivor House; David Huw Stephens; Practical Alternatives.
A good synopsis of the unique houses they are starting to build.

The Third Wave; Alvin Toffler; Collins.
An eye-opening look at the impact of technology on our future.

Use Your Head; Tony Buzan; BBC Publications.
The best part is on how to use organic charts rather than linear lists.

Wild Food; Roger Philips; Pan.
Organised seasonally with excellent pictures and great recipes.

INDEX

including species list